REVISE BTEC TECH AWARD

Sport, Activity and Fitness

PRACTICE ASSESSMENTS Plus+

Series Consultant: Harry Smith
Author: Sue Hartigan

A note from the publisher

These practice assessments are designed to complement your revision and to help prepare you for the external assessment. They do not include all the content and skills needed for the complete course and have been written to help you practise what you have learned. They may not be representative of a real assessment.

While the publishers have made every attempt to ensure that advice on the qualification and its assessment is accurate, the official specification and associated assessment guidance materials are the only authoritative source of information and should always be referred to for definitive guidance.

This qualification is reviewed on a regular basis and may be updated in the future. Any such updates that affect the content of this book will be outlined at **www.pearsonfe.co.uk/BTECchanges**.

Published by Pearson Education Limited, 80 Strand, London, WC2R ORL.
www.pearsonschoolsandfecolleges.co.uk

Copies of official specifications for all Pearson qualifications may be found on the website: qualifications.pearson.com

Typeset, produced and illustrated by QBS Learning Ltd
Cover illustration by Eoin Coveney

First published 2019
22 21 20 19
10 9 8 7 6 5 4 3 2 1

British Library Cataloguing in Publication Data
A catalogue record for this book is available from the British Library

ISBN 978 1 292 30698 8

Acknowledgements

1: McCardle, W. et al. Extract from *Essentials of Exercise Physiology* (2nd Edition). © Lippincott Williams and Wilkins, 2000; **17, 33, 49**: Davis, B. et al. Extract from *Physical Education and the Study of Sport* (4th Edition). © Harcourt Publishers, 2000. pp123–124.

Printed in Slovakia by Neografia

Notes from the publisher

1. While the publishers have made every attempt to ensure that advice on the qualification and its assessment is accurate, the official specification and associated assessment guidance materials are the only authoritative source of information and should always be referred to for definitive guidance. Pearson examiners have not contributed to any sections in this resource relevant to examination papers for which they have responsibility.

2. Pearson has robust editorial processes, including answer and fact checks, to ensure the accuracy of the content in this publication, and every effort is made to ensure this publication is free of errors. We are, however, only human, and occasionally errors do occur. Pearson is not liable for any misunderstandings that arise as a result of errors in this publication, but it is our priority to ensure that the content is accurate. If you spot an error, please do contact us at resourcescorrections@pearson.com so we can make sure it is corrected.

Websites

Pearson Education Limited is not responsible for the content of any external internet sites. It is essential for tutors to preview each website before using it in class so as to ensure that the URL is still accurate, relevant and appropriate. We suggest that tutors bookmark useful websites and consider enabling students to access them through the school/college intranet.

Introduction

This book has been designed to help you to practise the skills you may need for the external assessment of BTEC Tech Award **Sport, Activity and Fitness,** Component 2: The Principles of Training, Nutrition and Psychology for Sport and Activity.

About the practice assessments

The book contains four practice assessments for the component. Unlike your actual assessment, the questions have targeted hints, guidance and support in the margin to help you understand how to tackle them:

links to relevant pages in the Pearson Revise BTEC Tech Award Sport, Activity and Fitness Revision Guide so you can revise the essential content. This will also help you to understand how the essential content is applied to different contexts when assessed.

to get you started and remind you of the skills or knowledge you need to apply.

to help you on how to approach a question, such as making a brief plan.

to provide content that you need to learn such as a definition or principles related to training, nutrition and psychology.

to help you avoid common pitfalls.

to remind you of content related to the question to aid your revision on that topic.

for use with the final practice assessment to help you become familiar with answering in a given time and ways to think about allocating time for different questions.

There is space for you to write your answers to the questions within this book. However, if you require more space to complete your answers, you may want to use separate paper.

There is also an answer section at the back of the book, so you can check your answers for each practice assessment.

Check the Pearson website

For overarching guidance on the official assessment outcomes and key terms used in your assessment, please refer to the specification on the Pearson website. Check also whether you must have a calculator in your assessment.

The practice questions, support and answers in this book are provided to help you to revise the essential content in the specification, along with ways of applying your skills. Details of your actual assessment may change, so always make sure you are up to date on its format and requirements by asking your tutor or checking the Pearson website for the most up-to-date Sample Assessment Material, Mark Schemes and any past papers.

Contents

A small bit of small print

Pearson publishes Sample Assessment Material and the specification on its website. This is the official content and this book should be used in conjunction with it. The questions have been written to help you test your knowledge and skills. Remember: the real assessment may not look like this.

Practice assessment 1

Answer ALL questions.
Write your answers in the spaces provided.

1 Raj takes part in the sit and reach test. His sit and reach test score is **11 cm**.

Table 1 shows the normative test data for the sit and reach test.

	Category				
Gender	**Excellent**	**Above average**	**Average**	**Below average**	**Very poor**
Male	>20	19.9–14.1	14.0	13.9–9.1	<9
Female	>25	24.9–15.1	15.0	14.9–10.1	<10

Table 1

(a) Identify, using **Table 1**, Raj's rating for the sit and reach test.

....

....

1 mark

(b) State the component of fitness tested by the sit and reach test.

....

....

1 mark

Total for Question 1 = 2 marks

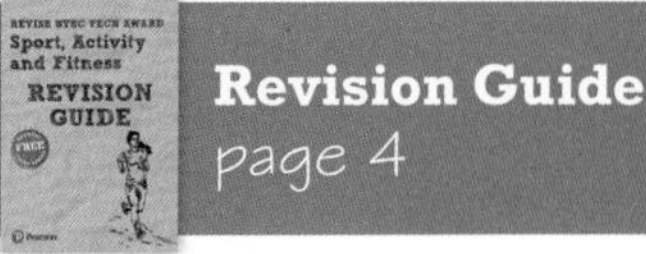

Revision Guide page 4

Hint

When you **identify**, you assess factual information. An answer might be a single word, although sometimes a few words or a maximum of a single sentence are required.

Hint

When you **state**, you give a definition or example – here, the appropriate component of fitness.

LEARN IT!

The symbol **>** means **greater than**. The symbol **<** means **less than**. For Table 1, a male scoring more than 20 (>20) rates excellent, or less than 9 (<9) rates very poor.

Explore

As well as the sit and reach test, make sure you know the following tests: Cooper 12-minute run (aerobic endurance), one-minute sit-up test (muscular endurance), hand grip dynamometer test (strength), Sargent jump test (power), 30-metre sprint test (speed). Consider how well each test design allows it to measure the component of fitness.

Revision Guide pages 14, 43

Hint

Sprint hurdling is where athletes run as fast as they can and also jump to clear a number of hurdles as they run.

Hint

If asked to **name** a training method, recall the correct name from the specification. For example, two training methods to improve **strength** would be 'free weights' and 'resistance machines'.

Hint

Give valid reasons for your chosen training methods to improve the power of a sprint hurdler. For example, if the sport was rowing which requires strength, a method could be 'Using free weights'. A reason could be 'It involves lifting heavy weights such as a deadlift. This improves strength so the rower can exert more force on each stroke of the oar.'

Hint

For Question 2(b), remember that extrinsic motivation can be provided through tangible and intangible rewards.

2 Pete is a sprint hurdler. He uses two different training methods to improve his power.

(a) Name **two** training methods Pete could use to improve his power and for each method give a reason why it is suitable to improve power for his sport.

Method of training 1

....

....

Reason

....

....

2 marks

Method of training 2

....

....

Reason

....

....

2 marks

Pete needs motivating to train to improve his power.

(b) State two examples of how Pete may be extrinsically motivated to take part in training to improve his power.

1 ....

....

1 mark

2 ....

....

1 mark

Pete benefits from his increased levels of motivation as it means he works harder in training and increases the intrinsic and extrinsic rewards he receives.

(c) Give **two other** benefits of Pete having high motivation levels for his participation in training.

1 ....

....

1 mark

2 ....

....

1 mark

Total for Question 2 = 8 marks

Revision Guide page 44

Hint

When you **give**, you provide examples, justifications and/or reasons to a context. Here, you need to give two other benefits of having a higher level of motivation when training.

Hint

Relate your answers to the scenario in the question by linking the theory of the benefits of motivation to the effect they will have on someone training.

LEARN IT!

Motivation is defined as the internal mechanisms and external stimuli that arouse and direct behaviour.

Watch out!

Refer to the information you have been given previously. Two possible benefits are already given in the introduction to the question. Make sure you chose two **different** benefits for your answers.

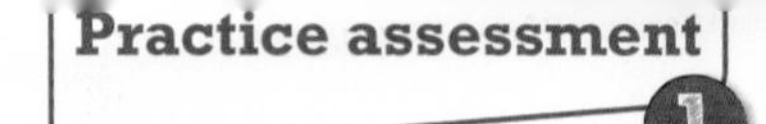

Revision Guide page 28

Hint

You are given information about the main activity and the time spent on it for each session. Use this information to help you decide on your answers.

Hint

For Question 3 (a), the principles of training are the 'rules' followed to make sure training is effective. For example, progressive overload should be applied by gradually making the training harder. This could be through increasing the time spent exercising, but this isn't happening here as each session is 25 minutes.

Hint

For Question 3 (b), think about the type of training that lasts 25 minutes.

Hint

A participant's session plan should give information about all of the parts of the session, not only the warm-up and main activity. One component is missing which you need to know to answer Question 3 (c).

3 **Table 2** shows Ivan's weekly training plan.

Session number	Warm-up	Main activity	Time spent on main activity
1	Pulse raiser, joint mobilisation and stretching	Running on a treadmill at a constant pace	25 minutes
2	Pulse raiser, joint mobilisation and stretching	Fartlek training session in the park	25 minutes
3	Pulse raiser, joint mobilisation and stretching	Swimming continuous lengths in the pool	25 minutes

Table 2

Use the information in **Table 2** to answer Questions 3 (a) to (c).

(a) Identify the principle of training Ivan is applying in his training.

....

....

1 mark

(b) Identify the component of fitness Ivan is working on in this training plan.

....

....

1 mark

(c) State **one other** component Ivan should include in his session plan.

....

....

1 mark

Ivan has a good level of self-confidence.

(d) Give the type of motivation that is increased when self-confidence increases.

....

....

1 mark

(e) Explain **two other** benefits of Ivan increasing his self-confidence.

1 ....

....

....

....

2 marks

2 ....

....

....

....

2 marks

Revision Guide pages 43, 45

LEARN IT!

Self-confidence is defined as the belief that a desired behaviour can be performed.

LEARN IT!

There are two different types of motivation. Intrinsic motivation is motivation that comes from internal factors. Extrinsic motivation is when external factors provide the motivation.

Hint

When answering Question 3 (e) you need to explain **two other** benefits. You are given one benefit in Question 3 (d). Do **not** repeat that motivation increases when Ivan's self-confidence increases.

Hint

When you **explain**, you convey understanding by making a point/statement or by linking the point/statement with a justification/expansion. Here, you should make each point by identifying a benefit and then expanding on each point to show the impact on training performance.

Revision Guide page 46

Hint

A **positive environment** is where performers feel safe, are happy to take risks and try new things and don't worry if they get it wrong. Consider how coaches create this for their players.

Hint

When you **explain** for this question, you should make each point by identifying a valid way of creating a positive environment in a physical training situation and then expand each point to show how this increases self-confidence.

Explore

Think about the things your teacher or coach does to make you feel more confident about trying something new or difficult. Consider further ways to increase self-confidence in a sporting performance, such as working with a training partner of similar ability, using goal setting or self-talk.

(f) Explain **two** ways a coach can increase Ivan's self-confidence through creating a positive environment for Ivan to train in.

1 ....

....

....

....

2 marks

2 ....

....

....

....

2 marks

Total for Question 3 = 12 marks

4 Tahlia carries out plyometric training each week to improve her power in volleyball.

She uses a 4 kg medicine ball during the plyometric drills.

(a) For each of the selected FITT principles:

(i) Give a definition

(ii) Give **one** example of how the principle could be applied to Tahlia's training.

Definition of intensity

....

....

1 mark

Example

....

....

1 mark

Definition of type

....

....

1 mark

Example

....

....

1 mark

Revision Guide pages 17–18

Hint

In this question, the command word **give** is for a definition and an example. In your example, demonstrate you understand the term by giving key features. For example, if asked to give an example of how continuous training could be applied, mention that the heart rate should be at 60–80% heart rate maximum (HRM) and training at a constant intensity for at least 30 minutes.

Hint

Examples should be linked to the scenario, with expansion to clarify how they relate to the scenario. Here, the example must be applied to Thalia's training in plyometrics.

LEARN IT!

There are four FITT principles: Frequency, Intensity, Time, Type.

Explore

Consider how someone using **two** other methods of training would apply all aspects of the FITT principles. Think about how the application of the FITT principles changes with different types of training methods, for example, circuit training and continuous training.

Revision Guide pages 24–25

Hint

Think about how the new information given to you in this question can be used to help your answer.

Hint

Consider why Tahlia chose plyometric training rather than Crossfit® which is a more generalised method of training to increase different components of fitness, not just power.

Hint

When working powerfully you tend to be working flat out for that period of time. Think about how this might affect your heart rate and therefore your training zone.

Explore

Crossfit® uses equipment from a number of different fitness disciplines. Apart from power, consider what else Crossfit® can be used to improve.

Tahlia's fitness test results show that her power is improving but is still a weakness. Two of the principles of training Tahlia uses to help improve her power are participant differences and needs and training zones.

(b) For each principle of training:

(i) Give a definition

(ii) Give **one** example of how the principle could be applied to Tahlia's future training sessions.

Participant differences and needs

....

....

1 mark

Example

....

....

1 mark

Training zones

....

....

1 mark

Example

....

....

1 mark

Total for Question 4 = 8 marks

5 Maya is a tennis player. Her coach thinks that with the right diet she could play even better.

She is thoughtful about her diet, eating nuts and seeds for protein and making sure she eats a good mix of vitamins and minerals.

(a) State the recommended daily calorie intake for an adult female.

....

.... calories (kcal)

1 mark

(b) Identify **one** other source of protein that Maya should eat as part of her diet.

....

....

1 mark

(c) Explain **one** reason why Maya should eat protein as part of her diet.

....

....

....

....

2 marks

Maya also eats a large amount of unsaturated fats in her diet.

(d) Give **one** example of an unsaturated fat that Maya might eat as part of her evening meal.

....

....

1 mark

Revision Guide page 39

Hint

To help understand what each question requires, you could use 'CUBE':

- **C**ircle the command verb
- **U**nderline key information in the question
- **B**ox key information in the case study
- **E**nsure you know what the question is asking you.

Hint

The recommended daily allowance (RDA) for an adult male is 2500 calories. Men often use more calories than women as they normally have more muscle mass, so you would expect a woman's RDA to be lower than this.

Watch out!

In Question 5 (b) a 'source' means what best to eat to get protein. The sources seeds and nuts are in the introduction to the question. Your answer must be **one other** source.

Hint

For Question 5 (c), think about the functions of protein and why a sports performer might need more than someone not taking part in sport.

Revision Guide pages 36–37

Hint

Limit is another word for restrict. The question is asking why Maya shouldn't eat too much fat. Although she should have fat in her diet, think about a problem Maya could have if she eats too much fat.

Hint

Think about the benefits of vitamin A, and which benefits are particularly important to a tennis player.

Explore

Consider the different types of diets that might suit different kinds of athletes and sports performers, and the reasons why.

(e) Explain why Maya should limit the amount of fats she eats in her diet.

....

....

....

....

2 marks

(f) State **one** reason why vitamin A is important in Maya's diet for her sport.

....

....

1 mark

Total for Question 5 = 8 marks

6 Declan competes in marathon races. He makes sure he takes the water offered to him during the race.

(a) Name the condition caused by not drinking enough water.

....

....

1 mark

Poor hydration will affect how well Declan can perform.

(b) Give **two** negatives of poor hydration.

1 ....

....

2 ....

....

2 marks

(c) Explain **one** benefit of good hydration for Declan during the marathon.

....

....

....

....

2 marks

Declan also drinks other fluids during the marathon.

(d) Explain **one other** fluid Declan may drink while running in the marathon.

....

....

....

....

2 marks

Total for Question 6 = 7 marks

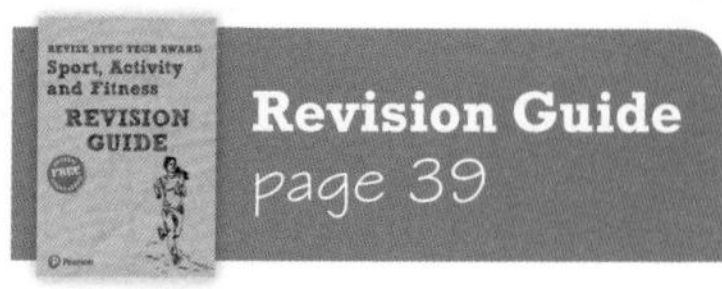

Revision Guide
page 39

LEARN IT!

A marathon is a long-distance race. Marathon runners race for 26.2 miles.

Hint

For Question 6 (b), you need to think about the potential problems for the body if it doesn't get enough liquid. Water is used throughout the body, for example to help blood flow and in temperature regulation.

LEARN IT!

The recommended daily intake (RDI) of fluids is two litres. However, if you are exercising you need one additional litre of fluid for each hour of exercise.

Hint

For Question 6 (d), consider whether any of the different sports drinks on sale would be useful in a long-distance race of over 26 miles, especially if the athlete is getting tired.

Revision Guide page 42

Hint

When you **discuss**, you consider the different aspects in detail of an issue, situation, problem or argument and how they interrelate.

LEARN IT!

A pre-workout supplement is any supplement taken before exercise in an attempt to increase workout performance. Creatine is a protein supplement.

Prepare

You could make a brief plan for longer answers. Here is an example.

Discuss

- the suitability of each supplement
- whether there is any value in Ethan taking them before a training session, and whether they are dependent on each other to bring about the desired effect
- any risks
- any alternatives, for example snacks.

Watch out!

Show your knowledge and understanding by correctly using specialist terminology and detail in your discussion that links back to the context of the question. Give reasons to support the points in your discussion.

7 Ethan is a weightlifter. He trains four times a week. Before every training session, he takes legal, pre-workout supplements.

Table 3 shows the pre-workout supplements that Ethan takes.

Ethan's pre-workout supplements
Caffeine
Glucose tablets
Creatine

Table 3

Discuss the suitability of Ethan's use of pre-workout supplements before his training sessions.

9 marks

Revision Guide page 42

Total for Question 7 = 9 marks

Hint

For longer answers, you could use PEEL. For example, in relation to caffeine:

Point: Make one point (for example why caffeine supplements are suitable).

Explain: Explain this point (for example how the function of caffeine helps in training).

Evidence: Justify the point and explanation. (for example the effect on Ethan to develop his weightlifting).

Link: Link back to the question (for example how this develops and improves Ethan's performance).

Hint

Consider whether there are any risks to taking these pre-workout supplements, or whether there is a better way to get the same outcome in training.

Hint

Plan a pre-workout snack that could effectively replace Ethan's pre-workout supplements.

Hint

Consider popular brands of different pre-workout supplements, those that use blends in their products and any potential issue with proprietary blends.

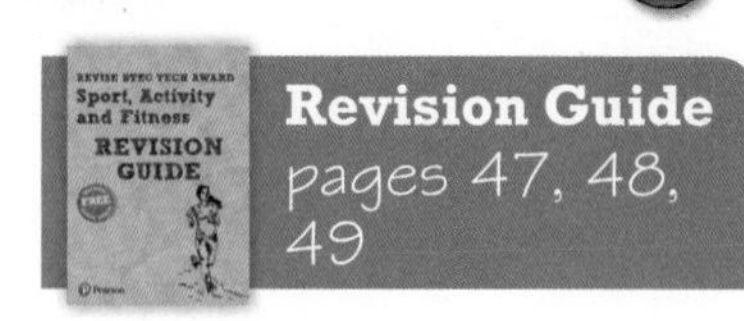

Revision Guide pages 47, 48, 49

LEARN IT!

There are two types of anxiety: **state anxiety** and **trait anxiety**.

LEARN IT!

State anxiety is situation specific. This means the player only gets anxious in certain situations.

Hint

In your explanation for Question 8 (b), state what the effect is likely to be on Aiden's state anxiety and expand on what he might be worried about.

Hint

Look at the key words in questions. In Question 8 (c), the words '**two**' and '**before**' are both in bold to draw your attention to them.

8 Aiden's football team are in the semi-finals of a regional competition. Aiden is worried about the game, as his team normally draw with their opponents. If they draw in the competition, five players from each team will have to take a penalty. The team with the most penalties scored will win.

(a) Give the definition of trait anxiety.

....

....

1 mark

(b) Explain the effect on Aiden's state anxiety if the teams draw in the semi-final.

....

....

....

....

2 marks

(c) Explain **two** methods Aiden's coach could use to reduce the anxiety levels of her players **before** the match.

1 ....

....

....

....

2 marks

2 ....

....

....

....

2 marks

Total for Question 8 = 7 marks

9 Jenna is a swimmer who trains regularly with her swimming club.

She does well on short-distance races but gets tired during long-distance races, often finishing last.

Evaluate which one of the following training methods Jenna should use to improve her aerobic endurance for swimming:

- Interval training
- Fartlek training.

9 marks

Revision Guide page 9

Hint

When you **evaluate,** you consider various aspects of a subject's qualities in relation to its context, such as: strengths and weaknesses, advantages and disadvantages, pros and cons. You need to come to a judgement supported by evidence, which will often be in the form of a conclusion.

Watch out!

Interval training can be adapted to develop speed or aerobic endurance. Your evaluation should focus on **aerobic endurance.**

Prepare

You could make a brief plan for longer answers. Here is an example.

- Demonstrate knowledge of the two training methods.
- Evaluate some advantages and disadvantages and how easily each could improve aerobic endurance for swimming.
- Conclude by making a judgement about which should be used, evaluating competing points.

Hint

Throughout your evaluation, relate your answer back to the sport in the question to ensure your comments are relevant to the question context.

Revision Guide
page 9

Hint

For longer answers, you could use PEEL. For example, in relation to Fartlek training:

Point: Make one point (for example what Fartlek training is).

Explain: Explain this point (for example how it can improve the component of fitness Jenna requires).

Evidence: Justify the point and explanation (for example how it relates to Jenna's sport and how far it is of use compared to interval training).

Link: Link back to the question (for example, considering pros and cons, and which method is most beneficial for Jenna's sport and aims).

Watch out!

Your evaluation should show breadth and not be too brief so be familiar with a range of sports. Use paragraphs to develop a logical evaluation.

Hint

Conclude your well-developed and logical evaluation with a judgement on the most appropriate training method.

....

....

....

....

....

....

....

....

....

....

....

....

....

....

....

....

....

....

....

....

....

....

....

....

....

....

....

Total for Question 9 = 9 marks

TOTAL FOR PRACTICE ASSESSMENT = 70 MARKS

Practice assessment 2

Answer ALL questions.
Write your answers in the spaces provided.

1 Abena is a rock climber. She takes part in a hand grip dynamometer test. Her result is **39 kg**.

Table 1 shows the normative test data of the grip dynamometer test for males and females.

	Category				
Gender	**Excellent**	**Good**	**Average**	**Fair**	**Poor**
Male	>56 kg	51–56 kg	45–50 kg	39–44 kg	<39 kg
Female	>36 kg	31–36 kg	25–30 kg	19–24 kg	<19 kg

Table 1

(a) Identify the category Abena is in for the grip dynamometer test, using **Table 1**.

....

....

1 mark

(b) State the component of fitness tested by the grip dynamometer test.

....

....

1 mark

Total for Question 1 = 2 marks

Revision Guide
pages 1, 6

Watch out!

Read the question and Table 1 carefully. Don't just use the first row of data. Make sure you read the row in the table that gives the **female** scores.

Hint

When you **identify**, you assess factual information that may require a single-word answer, although sometimes a few words or a maximum of a single sentence are required.

Hint

When you **state**, you give a definition or example. When stating the component of fitness, think about the technique used to complete the dynamometer test. For example, you have to squeeze the grip as hard as you can for about five seconds, so this can't be a test of power as it is not explosive.

Revision Guide pages 9, 14, 47

Hint

When you **name**, you give a definition or example. Here, you are naming training methods.

Hint

Aerobic endurance training improves the ability of the cardiorespiratory system to transport oxygen and nutrients to the working muscles so the body can work for longer. **Power** involves explosive movement. Think of a training method that uses this type of movement.

Hint

When you **describe**, you give an account or details. Here, it needs to be clear from your description what the main features of the training method are.

Hint

When you **give**, you can provide examples, justifications and/or reasons to a context. Here, you give a definition of anxiety.

LEARN IT!

There are two types of anxiety. **State** refers to anxiety in a particular situation. **Trait** refers to a characteristic of someone's personality as always being anxious.

2 Owen joins a boxing club. In the first training session, he completes a number of fitness tests.

The test results show that his aerobic endurance and power are both poor.

(a) Complete **Table 2** by:

(i) naming **one** training method to improve each of these components of fitness

(ii) describing how to carry out each of the training methods chosen.

Component of fitness	**(i) Training method**	**(ii) Description of training method**
Aerobic endurance	1 mark	1 mark
Power	1 mark	1 mark

Table 2

Owen enjoys the first training session but is anxious about sparring with other boxers.

(b) Give a definition of anxiety.

....

....

1 mark

To help control Owen's anxiety, the boxing coach decides to use an induction and to place Owen in a group based on his ability level.

(c) Explain how these methods can be used to control Owen's anxiety.

Induction

....

....

....

....

2 marks

Ability level

....

....

....

....

2 marks

Total for Question 2 = 9 marks

Revision Guide page 49

Hint

When you **explain**, you convey understanding by making a point/statement or by linking the point/statement with a justification/expansion. Here, you need to make a point about the method as applied to Owen and then justify how using this method will reduce his anxiety.

Explore

Think about other ways the coach could help control Owen's anxiety. For example, by using music that lowers his anxiety levels and motivates him to participate or a pre-fight talk to reassure him and reduce worry.

Explore

Consider whether all methods of controlling anxiety would work equally well with everyone, or if different situations mean different methods should be used. Make sure you can apply this knowledge to a range of suitable sporting activities.

Revision Guide page 17

Hint

When you **calculate**, you determine the amount or number mathematically. You are given the units for the answer (bpm). This should help you think about the formula you need to use for this equation.

Watch out!

Make sure you show your answer to **both** parts of the question. Under **calculation** show the equation for carrying out the calculation, even though it is a very straightforward sum to work out, **and** the answer.

Hint

For Question 3 (b), consider how the pulse is measured by using two fingers to lightly compress the radial and carotid arteries where they pass close to the surface of the skin.

Explore

Consider another way Ali could measure his training intensity and the different types of technology available for him to use.

3 Ali is taking part in a fartlek training session. During the less intense parts of his run he rates his training intensity as 15, using the rate of perceived exertion (RPE) scale.

(a) Calculate Ali's heart rate using his rate of perceived exertion (RPE).

Calculation

....

Answer .... bpm

2 marks

(b) Name the **two** locations on his body where Ali could take his pulse to check his heart rate.

1 ....

....

2 ....

....

2 marks

Ali is trying to improve his performance in athletics as he is close to gaining the secondary school silver award for athletics. He is motivated to train because he wants this award.

(c) State the **type** of motivation causing Ali to train.

....

....

1 mark

Motivation can also be given through the use of intangible rewards.

(d) State the meaning of the term 'intangible reward'.

....

....

1 mark

(e) Give **two** examples of intangible rewards.

1 ....

....

2 ....

....

2 marks

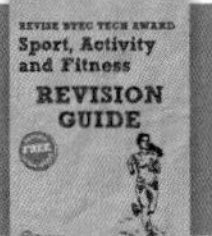

Revision Guide page 43

Hint

When you **state**, you give a definition or example. To state the type of motivation, think about where the motivation is coming from – whether it is coming from **the person** or an **external source.** When stating the meaning of a term, give a definition.

Watch out!

When you **give**, you can provide examples, justifications and/or reasons to a context. Link each example to the question context by thinking of intangible rewards an **athlete** may receive.

Explore

Consider whether the types of rewards change depending on the level of play for different sports, for example, an amateur football player and a footballer paid to play.

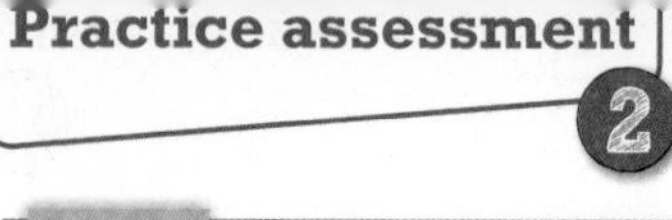

Revision Guide page 43, 44

LEARN IT!

Motivation is defined as the internal mechanisms and external stimuli that arouse and direct behaviour.

Hint

You are given two different benefits that both relate to improving performance. In your answer, think of two **different** ways that performance could be improved so your answers do not overlap.

Explore

Consider factors that affect motivation levels and their impact in different sports. For example:

- when professional performers seem highly motivated within a game and what may contribute to this higher level of motivation
- how an increase in self-confidence could affect an individual's motivation levels
- three other benefits of increased motivation on fitness participation levels: increased intensity of effort, overcoming adversity and higher enjoyment levels.

Ali's coach has been working to improve Ali's motivation.

Two benefits of increased motivation are:

- continuing to take part on a regular basis
- increased intrinsic and extrinsic rewards.

(f) Explain how these benefits will improve Ali's performance during a fitness training programme.

Continuing to take part

....

....

....

....

2 marks

Increased rewards

....

....

....

....

2 marks

Total for Question 3 = 12 marks

4 Hawani uses the percentage of her maximum heart rate to make sure she is working at the intended intensity in the different parts of her training session.

(a) Name the training zone where the percentage of maximum heart rate should be 50–60%.

....

....

1 mark

Hawani applies the FITT principle to her training.

(b) Give the definition of frequency.

....

....

1 mark

Hawani plans her training sessions carefully as she is aware of the possibility of overtraining.

(c) Describe the training principle of overtraining.

....

....

....

....

2 marks

Revision Guide pages 16, 22, 25

Hint

The higher the percentage of maximum heart rate the greater the intensity someone is working at. The percentage of maximum heart rate given is quite low, so think about an activity within a session where intensity is at its lowest.

Hint

Hawani might apply the FITT principles as follows:

- Frequency – she increases the number of training days from one to two a week
- Intensity – she uses training zones to ensure she is working at the right level
- Time – she extends the training session length from 30 to 40 minutes
- Type – she improves her aerobic endurance through continuous training.

Hint

For Question 4 (c), consider that training programmes should have rest days built into them to avoid overtraining.

Explore

Think about why a sprinter and a marathon runner train using different training zones.

Revision Guide pages 20, 24

Hawani applies the principle of specificity to her training programme.

(d) Describe the principle of specificity.

....

....

....

....

2 marks

(e) Identify the principle of training from the following description.

Choosing a component of fitness that needs to be trained based on someone's personal fitness test data and the sport they are participating in.

....

....

1 mark

Total for Question 4 = 7 marks

Hint

When you **describe**, you need to give an account or details of something or give an account of a process. Here, you need to give two details about the principle of specificity so that it is clear to whoever is reading your description what is being described.

Watch out!

The descriptions of two different principles of training make reference to the training being relevant to the sport, but only **one** also mentions the use of **personal fitness test data.** This can help you differentiate between the two training methods.

Explore

If planning a training programme for your sport, consider how you might apply each of the principles of training while ensuring overtraining and reversibility do not take place.

5 Paul is taking part in the Great North Run. He is training regularly to make sure he is fit enough to take part and complete this half marathon. On the days Paul trains, he increases his fluid intake.

(a) State the recommended increase in fluid intake per hour of exercise.

.... litre(s)

1 mark

(b) It is important to increase fluid intake to maintain hydration.

(i) Describe **one negative** effect of poor hydration on Paul's blood plasma.

....

....

....

....

2 marks

(ii) Explain the effect this will have on Paul's performance in training.

....

....

....

....

2 marks

Revision Guide
page 39

Prepare

Know about a range of sports and sporting activities. A half marathon is a long-distance race. It is 13.1 miles in length, so is half the distance of a marathon.

LEARN IT!

Plasma is the liquid part of the blood.

Hint

A negative effect is another way of asking for a disadvantage or problem. So think about a problem that would happen if the water content in blood plasma was reduced.

Hint

If blood plasma becomes less liquid, think about the effect on its ability to transport oxygen and nutrients.

Revision Guide page 39

Watch out!

Read the question carefully. It already provides one possible answer. Make sure that your answer explains a reason **other** than 'a reduction in blood plasma volume'.

LEARN IT!

Dehydration is defined as a harmful reduction in the amount of fluid in the body.

LEARN IT!

To maintain hydration, the recommended daily fluid intake is two litres. This increases by one litre for every hour of exercise.

Explore

Consider a range of different sports that last for varying lengths of time and how each type of sports performer makes sure they remain hydrated during their activity.

(c) Explain **two** reasons, other than a reduction in blood plasma volume, why staying well hydrated will benefit Paul's half marathon performance.

1 ....

....

....

....

2 marks

2 ....

....

....

....

2 marks

Total for Question 5 = 9 marks

6 Maddie plays volleyball and is training to improve her explosive strength. To be healthy, she needs to include the correct percentages of macronutrients in her diet.

(a) State the percentage of her dietary intake that should be protein.

.... %

1 mark

There are many different protein sources Maddie could include in her diet.

(b) Identify **one** food source of protein.

....

....

1 mark

(c) Explain why the function of protein will benefit Maddie and her sporting performance.

....

....

....

....

2 marks

(d) Name the **two** categories of amino acids that make up protein.

1 ....

....

2 ....

....

2 marks

Total for Question 6 = 6 marks

Revision Guide pages 34, 35

LEARN IT!

Carbohydrates should form the largest percentage of our diet at 50%–60% of our diet. This leaves 40%–50% for fats **and** protein.

Watch out!

Don't confuse the percentages of fats and proteins. Even though too much fat is bad for us, we still need to eat more fat than protein in our diet.

Hint

For the Question 3 (c) **explain** question, **first** you need to identify a function of protein and **then** expand on this by applying the function to the question context – how the function would be useful to the volleyball player.

Explore

Think about how people with different dietary requirements can still get the protein they need. For example people who are vegetarians, vegans, lactose intolerant or gluten free.

Revision Guide
page 31, 37, 40

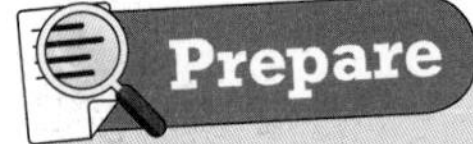

Hint

For this **analyse** question, examine the table methodically to explain which foods contain the required vitamins and how the function of each would help a badminton player.

Prepare

You could make a brief plan for longer answers. Here is an example:

- analyse Layla's food intake and state which **food source** provides her with each essential vitamin
- analyse the **function** of each vitamin and **apply** it in context, for example why it benefits Layla's badminton performance and the effect of not taking each vitamin.

Hint

The question lists three vitamins and the table gives eight food sources, so choose wisely. For example:

- Liver is a good source for two of the vitamins but if you match each vitamin to a different source you show breadth of knowledge.
- Choose examples you are most confident about – you don't need to use every one.

7 Layla plays badminton.

Table 3 shows her food intake on a typical day.

Breakfast	Lunch	Dinner
Cereal	Tuna sushi	Liver and bacon
Skimmed milk	An orange	Potato
		An apple

Table 3

Micronutrients are a vital part of a healthy diet and can be beneficial to performance during sport.

Analyse, using **Table 3**, how Layla's dietary intake of vitamin A, vitamin C and vitamin D will benefit her performance as a badminton player.

9 marks

....

....

....

....

....

....

....

....

....

....

....

....

....

....

....

....

....

....

....

Total for Question 7 = 9 marks

Revision Guide pages 31, 37, 40

Hint

For longer answers, use PEEL. For example, in relation to vitamin A:

Point: make one point (for example a source of vitamin A in Layla's diet).

Explain: Explain this point (for example how a function of vitamin A helps Layla in badminton).

Evidence: Justify the point and explanation (for example why this is a benefit for Layla's performance).

Link: Link back to the question (for example the impact on Layla's performance of not taking the amount of vitamin A needed in her diet).

Hint

Sushi is uncooked, fresh fish on boiled white rice. When tuna is fresh (not canned) it is considered an oily fish.

Explore

Consider what else a badminton player should include in their diet to ensure they are healthy enough to exercise. Learn the food sources stated in the specification for macronutrients and micronutrients so you can identify them when presented with a performer's 'typical diet'.

Revision Guide
pages 47, 48

Hint

If asked to say how something **differs**, make sure your answer is clear. Here, for example, you could make it clear which type of anxiety you are talking about by structuring each different difference along the lines of: Trait anxiety is … whereas state anxiety is ….

Hint

You are told in the question that Finn is normally confident and that he only gets anxious in a specific situation. This should help you chose the correct type of anxiety he is experiencing.

LEARN IT!

Somatic anxiety is the physical effects of anxiety.

Explore

Consider how elite sports performers control their anxiety before they compete in an important event, such as 100 m sprinters, high-board divers, skiers before racing downhill or footballers before taking an important penalty.

8 Finn plays basketball. He is normally a confident player but becomes anxious when he has to take free throws at the basket. There are two types of anxiety: state and trait.

(a) State **two** ways that state and trait anxiety differ.

1 ……………………………………………………………………………………

……………………………………………………………………………………

2 ……………………………………………………………………………………

……………………………………………………………………………………

2 marks

(b) Explain which type of anxiety Finn is experiencing.

……………………………………………………………………………………

……………………………………………………………………………………

……………………………………………………………………………………

……………………………………………………………………………………

2 marks

The effects of anxiety can be classified as either cognitive or somatic.

(c) State the meaning of the term 'cognitive anxiety'.

……………………………………………………………………………………

……………………………………………………………………………………

1 mark

Increased heart rate and butterflies in the stomach are two somatic effects of anxiety.

(d) State **two other** somatic effects of anxiety.

1 ……………………………………………………………………………………

……………………………………………………………………………………

2 ……………………………………………………………………………………

……………………………………………………………………………………

2 marks

Total for Question 8 = 7 marks

9 Monica is a rugby player.

Figure 1 shows Monica's partially completed fitness programme.

Personal information			
Exercise availability:	**Health screening questionnaire results:**	**Activity dislikes:**	**Activity likes:**
Mon–Fri: after 6 p.m. Sunday: anytime	Asthma	Continuous training on roads	Any other training
Aim:			
Objective: To take part in four fartlek training sessions a week			
Components of fitness:		**Safe design:**	
Session plans			
Warm-up:	**Main activity:**	**Cool-down:**	

Figure 1

A fitness programme requires a set structure to ensure it is effective in achieving the aim of the participant.

Analyse the importance of using a person-centred approach and including aims and a warm-up in the structure of a fitness programme in order to improve Monica's fitness for rugby.

9 marks

....

....

....

....

....

....

....

....

....

....

....

....

....

Revision Guide pages 26, 27, 28

Hint

When you **analyse** for this question, you need to examine methodically the given structure of the fitness programme and explain how each aspect of the structure mentioned in the question (person-centred approach, aims and a warm-up), is likely to lead to an improvement in Monica's fitness for rugby.

Prepare

You could make a brief plan for longer answers. Here is an example.

- State a reason why each identified piece of **information** is required in a fitness programme.
- Analyse the **use** of each identified piece of information and **apply** it to the question context. Include why it benefits Monica's training and rugby performances, and the effect if the information is not included.

LEARN IT!

Questionnaires can be used to gather personal information to make sure the fitness programme has a person-centred approach. A PAR-Q is a type of health-screening questionnaire.

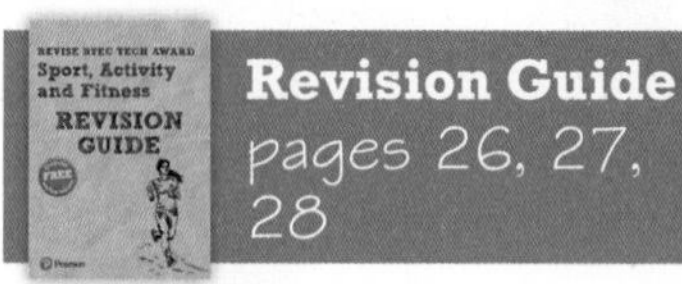

Revision Guide pages 26, 27, 28

Hint

For longer answers, use PEEL. For example, in relation to a person-centred approach:

Point: Make one point (for example how a person-centred approach captures preferences and availability).

Explain: Explain this point (for example what this shows about the training Monica likes and dislikes).

Evidence: Justify the point and explanation (for example how this enables selection of a training method that succeeds for Monica's aims).

Link: Link back to the question (for example the information is very important to ensure no missed sessions and that fitness and performance is improved).

LEARN IT!

There are **six** different pieces of information required for a fitness programme:

1 Personal information
2 Aims
3 Objectives
4 Appropriate components of fitness
5 Safe design
6 Components of the session plan (warm-up, main activity, cool-down).

....

....

....

....

....

....

....

....

....

....

....

....

....

....

....

....

....

....

....

....

....

....

....

....

....

Total for Question 9 = 9 marks

TOTAL FOR PRACTICE ASSESSMENT = 70 MARKS

Practice assessment 3

Answer ALL questions.
Write your answers in the spaces provided.

1 Jan takes part in the Sargent jump test. Her Sargent jump test score is **58.1 cm**.

Table 1 shows normative test data for the Sargent jump test for 16 to 19 year olds.

	Category				
Gender	**Excellent**	**Above average**	**Average**	**Below average**	**Very poor**
Male	>65 cm	50–65 cm	40–49 cm	30–39 cm	<30 cm
Female	>58 cm	47–58 cm	36–46 cm	26–35 cm	<26 cm

Table 1

(a) Using **Table 1**, identify Jan's rating for the Sargent jump test.

....

....

1 mark

(b) State the component of fitness tested by the Sargent jump test.

....

....

1 mark

Total for Question 1 = 2 marks

Revision Guide page 7

Hint

When you **identify**, you assess factual information. An answer might be a single word, although sometimes a few words or a maximum of a single sentence are required.

Hint

When you **state**, you give a definition or example – here, the appropriate component of fitness.

Hint

The Sargent jump test involves jumping as high as you can from standing. Think about the component of fitness you will need to use to lift your body explosively from the ground.

Prepare

Make sure you use key terminology from the specification. For example, the correct names for the six fitness tests and the components of fitness they test.

Explore

Make sure you can interpret data to determine the fitness levels for different target groups: girls and boys (14–16 years), men and women, elite performers and older people (65+).

Revision Guide page 10

Watch out!

The question states **muscular endurance**. Don't confuse this with cardiovascular endurance, which is the ability of the body to supply oxygen and nutrients to maintain performance without fatigue. You need a training method where the focus is on the **muscles working**.

Hint

If asked to **name** a training method, recall the correct name from the specification. For example, if asked to provide two training methods to improve aerobic endurance, the answers would be two of continuous training, fartlek training, interval training.

Hint

For each reason, make sure you make it clear **how** the training method will improve muscular endurance relevant to the rower.

Hint

Note the key word **physical** effects in Question 2 (b). You need to give examples of somatic anxiety.

2 Karar belongs to a rowing club. He uses two different training methods to improve his muscular endurance.

(a) Name **two** training methods he could use and for each method give a reason why it is suitable to improve muscular endurance for his sport.

Method of training 1

....

....

Reason

....

....

2 marks

Method of training 2

....

....

Reason

....

....

2 marks

Karar rows in a boat with three others. Karar never rows as well in a race as he does in training, because he becomes anxious in a competitive situation.

(b) State **two** examples of the physical effects of anxiety Karar may experience.

1 ....

....

1 mark

2 ....

....

1 mark

The rowing team's coach tries to reduce Karar's anxiety by giving him a pre-race team talk.

(c) Give **two other** methods the coach could use to help reduce Karar's anxiety.

1 ....

....

2 ....

....

2 marks

Total for Question 2 = 8 marks

Revision Guide page 49

Hint

When you **give**, you provide examples, justifications and/or reasons to a context. Here, you need to give **two** methods for reducing anxiety.

Watch out!

A possible method to reduce anxiety is already given in the introduction to the question. Make sure you chose two **other** methods for your answers.

Explore

The more familiar you are with different types of sports, the easier it will be for you to apply your knowledge to the different question contexts. Explore a range of contrasting sports and identify the components of fitness required and the training methods most likely to be used.

Revision Guide
page 17, 28

Hint

Look at the information you are given about the main activity. There is no information about the number of sets or reps Jenny completes. Think about what else has been used to measure activity levels.

Hint

Look at the differences you are given between work completed in week 1 and work completed in week 6. These differences should guide you to the correct answer for Question 3 (b).

Hint

Exercise places more demand on the body than sitting. It is important to prepare the body through a warm-up. For Question 3 (c), consider how changes take place when warming up, for example to the muscular and circulatory systems, and how this helps prepare the body for exercise.

3 **Table 2** shows the first and last week of Jenny's six-week training plan.

	Week 1	**Week 6**
Number of sessions each week	1	4
	Warm-up	Warm-up
Main activity	Free weights and resistance machines at 13 RPE	Free weights and resistance machines at 19 RPE
	Cool-down	Cool-down

Table 2

Use the information in **Table 2** to answer Questions 3 (a) to (c).

(a) Identify how Jenny is measuring the intensity of her training.

....

....

1 mark

(b) Identify **one** principle of training Jenny is applying in her training plan.

....

....

1 mark

(c) State **one** reason why Jenny warms up before each training session.

....

....

1 mark

Jenny is motivated to complete her training programme.

(d) Give the type of motivation being described.

'Jenny continues training because of the intangible rewards'.

1 mark

(e) Explain **two** benefits of high levels of intrinsic motivation to Jenny.

1

2 marks

2

2 marks

Revision Guide pages 43, 44

LEARN IT!

An intangible reward is a **non-physical** reward such as praise from a coach or recognition from others when you do something well.

Hint

Intrinsic motivation is the motivation we get from ourselves, not others.

Hint

When you **explain**, you convey understanding by making a point/statement or by linking the point/statement with a justification/expansion. Here, you should make each point by identifying a benefit and then expanding on each point to show the impact on training performance.

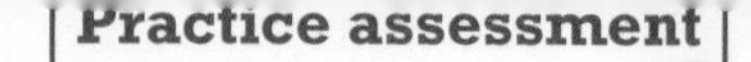

Revision Guide page 43

Hint

When you **explain** for this question, you should make each point by identifying a tangible reward then expanding on each point to show how the fitness instructor could use this to increase extrinsic motivation.

Watch out!

The question states **tangible rewards**. You need to focus on **only** those types of rewards in your answer.

LEARN IT!

Benefits of increased motivation on fitness participation levels include intensity of effort, regular participation, overcoming adversity, higher enjoyment levels and increased intrinsic and extrinsic rewards.

Explore

Too much reliance on extrinsic motivation would mean the sports performer might give up if the extrinsic motivation was removed, such as no longer being part of a winning team. Consider how most sportspeople are motivated by intrinsic **and** extrinsic motivation.

(f) Explain **two** ways a fitness instructor could use tangible rewards to increase Jenny's extrinsic motivation to train.

1 ....

....

....

....

2 marks

2 ....

....

....

....

2 marks

Total for Question 3 = 12 marks

4 Harin plays badminton. He carries out sport-specific speed training (SAQ®) for 45 minutes once a week to improve his speed on the badminton court.

(a) For each of the selected FITT principles:

(i) Give a definition

(ii) Give **one** example of how the principle could be applied to Harin's training.

Definition of time

....

....

1 mark

Example

....

....

1 mark

Definition of frequency

....

....

1 mark

Example

....

....

1 mark

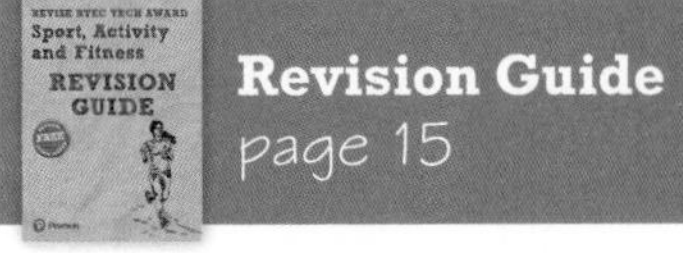
Revision Guide page 15

SAQ® training (speed, agility, quickness) involves sprinting and then changing direction. For badminton this could be short sprints from the middle of the court to each corner returning to the middle each time.

Prepare

Be familiar with a range of sports so you can apply the use of the different training methods to them. This will help you to apply your knowledge and give examples in your answers.

Explore

Consider other methods of training that can be used to develop speed for badminton such as:

- interval training – for example sprinting short distances across and around the court and counting the number of times before recovery is needed
- sprint training – for example using resistance bands
- sport-specific training – for example ladder drills to develop speed on the court.

Revision Guide pages 22, 23

Hint

Carefully read any new information given to you in a question. Here, for example, Harin increases his training load but becomes injured and has to stop training. This new information helps you answer the question.

LEARN IT!

You get fitter as the body adapts to extra work in training. These adaptations can make you stronger, faster and more powerful. The type of training determines the way the body adapts.

Watch out!

When selecting training methods, they should be suitable for the component of fitness to be improved **and** relevant to the sport. For example, if a games player and a marathon runner aim to improve aerobic endurance, fartlek training would suit a games player because of changes in pace, while continuous training would suit a marathon runner who runs mostly at a set pace.

Harin thinks he is taking too long to increase his speed. He decides to increase his training sessions, so he starts training every day.

(b) Harin becomes injured and has to stop training. The training principles of reversibility and overtraining have been applied to his training.

For each principle of training:

(i) Give a definition

(ii) Give **one** example of how the principle might apply to Harin's future training sessions.

Reversibility

....

....

1 mark

Example

....

....

1 mark

Overtraining

....

....

1 mark

Example

....

....

1 mark

Total for Question 4 = 8 marks

5 Mo is training for an Ironman competition. He trains three hours a day during the week and five hours on Saturdays. Mo is vegetarian and plans his diet carefully. Protein and vitamins are important parts of his diet.

(a) State the structure of protein.

....

....

1 mark

(b) Identify, **other** than meat, **one** source of protein that Mo could eat as part of his diet.

....

....

1 mark

(c) Explain **one** benefit to Mo of eating a protein meal after a training session.

....

....

....

....

2 marks

Mo also eats a large amount of fibre in his diet.

(d) Give **one** example of a source of food Mo should eat to ensure appropriate bowel emptying.

....

....

1 mark

Revision Guide pages 34, 35

Prepare

Make sure you are aware of a variety of sporting activities. An Ironman competition is a form of triathlon, but it is a very long race. Some Ironman competitions are 225 km (140 miles) long.

LEARN IT!

Protein should be 15% of the diet, the smallest percentage of any macronutrient in the diet. Proteins are made up of essential and non-essential amino acids and both must be in the diet. The body cannot make the eight essential amino acids.

Watch out!

Always read the question carefully. Question 5 (c) is asking for a benefit of eating protein **after** a training session. Think about what has happened to muscle during the session.

LEARN IT!

The main function of fibre is to help prevent constipation and haemorrhoids. Consuming foods high in fibre and the timing of food consumption aid the digestion process and bowel emptying before exercise.

Revision Guide pages 37, 41

Hint

Think about the possible disadvantages to a runner if they are carrying a lot of unnecessary food waste in the body when exercising.

Watch out!

Always relate your response to the question context. You need to think why it is important for a sports performer in an ironman race to have vitamin C.

LEARN IT!

Make sure you know the importance of vitamins A, B1, C and D to sports performers. For example, the function of vitamin B1 is to help convert food into energy. This is important to sports performers so they have enough energy for exercise.

Explore

Think about the timing of food intake for an athlete before, during and after an event and how to maximise their energy for training and competition.

(e) Explain **one** reason why bowel emptying would be important to Mo before his long race.

....

....

....

....

2 marks

(f) State **one** reason why vitamin C is important in Mo's diet for his sport.

....

....

1 mark

Total for Question 5 = 8 marks

6 Amber plays rugby. Her training is not going well as she is constantly tired and shows signs of dehydration. Her friend tells her she needs to eat more minerals in her diet.

(a) Name **one** food source of calcium.

....

....

1 mark

A lack of calcium in the diet will affect Amber's ability to play rugby.

(b) Give **two negatives** of a lack of calcium in Amber's diet.

1 ....

....

2 ....

....

2 marks

(c) Explain **one** benefit of an appropriate level of iron in Amber's diet.

....

....

....

....

2 marks

Amber's friend tells her bananas are a good source of minerals.

(d) Explain **one** reason why eating a daily banana is a good addition to Amber's diet.

....

....

....

....

2 marks

Total for Question 6 = 7 marks

Revision Guide page 38

Hint

You could underline or circle key words in questions in your exam paper. This can help you review your answer to make sure you have included all the important points.

Hint

A food source here means what Amber needs to eat to get the calcium she needs in her diet.

Watch out!

Always think about the nature of the sport in the question context. In Question 6 (b), you need to think about potential problems if the body doesn't get enough calcium and then relate this to a rugby player and the demands of the sport.

Explore

Explore the food sources Amber should eat to ensure an appropriate range of micronutrients to maintain her health and ability to train. Consider sources of the minerals potassium, iron and calcium and how the function of each will aid sports performance.

Revision Guide pages 39, 40

Hint

When you **discuss**, you consider the different aspects in detail of an issue, situation, problem or argument and how they interrelate. Here, discuss the suitability of Sabina's diet plan.

Hint

Look at the information in the question introduction and think about how you can use it. Here, for example, you are told that Sabina trains on Mondays and Wednesdays. Consider how this might impact on her nutritional needs.

Prepare

You could make a brief plan for longer answers. Here, there are a few approaches you could take. For example, you could talk about each day in turn, or each of the column headings in the table.

LEARN IT!

The recommended daily intake (RDI) of fluid is two litres. This increases by one litre for every hour of exercise.

7 Sabina produces a diet plan to allow her to train hard ready for her next gymnastics competition. She trains on Mondays and Wednesdays from 4 p.m. until 6 p.m.

Table 3 shows part of Sabina's diet plan.

Day	Carbohydrates %	Fats %	Protein %	Fluid intake (litres)	Total calories
Monday	55	30	15	4	2000
Tuesday	58	30	12	2	1990
Wednesday	58	30	12	4	1995
Thursday	55	30	15	2	2000

Table 3

Discuss the suitability of Sabina's diet plan to support her in training for her next gymnastics competition.

9 marks

....

....

....

....

....

....

....

....

....

....

....

....

....

....

....

....

....

....

Revision Guide pages 39, 40

Total for Question 7 = 9 marks

Hint

Try to avoid saying the same thing for each day of the week or each dietary factor. For example, if looking at the percentage carbohydrates, you might notice that all four days are within the same range and that this range is within the recommended daily allowance.

Hint

For longer answers, use PEEL. For example, in relation to calories:

Point: Make one point (for example the RDA of calories for women is 2000).

Explain: Explain this point (for example whether Sabina is eating less than the RDA).

Evidence: Justify the point and explanation (for example what this may mean in terms of weight loss and tiredness).

Link: Link back to the question (for example the suitability of balanced macronutrients; the impact of lack of energy to train).

Explore

Consider what else a gymnast should include in their diet to ensure they are healthy enough to exercise.

Revision Guide pages 45, 46

Hint

To answer the **explain** Question 8 (b), **first** identify a benefit of self-confidence and **then** expand on it, linking to the question context and thinking about how the benefit will improve Isla's hockey performance.

Hint

You could circle and underline key words in the question. For Question 8 (c), '**two**' is clearly important as it is in bold, but '**goal setting**' is also important and is the focus for your response.

LEARN IT!

Goals are what people want to achieve, giving them something to aim for.

Explore

Goals should be SMART: specific, measurable, achievable, realistic and time-framed. Goals can be short term or long term. Think about short-term and long-term goals for different sportspeople, for example, footballers.

8 Isla is a goalkeeper for a hockey team. The team need to win the next match to stay in the division. Although the opposition are a good team, Isla has been using goal setting to increase her self-confidence ready for the match.

(a) Give the definition of self-confidence.

....

....

1 mark

(b) Explain the effect of Isla's self-confidence on her hockey performance.

....

....

....

....

2 marks

(c) Explain **two** ways goal setting can lead to an increase in Isla's self-confidence.

1 ....

....

....

....

2 marks

2 ....

....

....

....

2 marks

Total for Question 8 = 7 marks

9 James is a sprint hurdler. He wants to improve his time in the 110 m hurdles but to do so he needs to improve his flexibility.

Evaluate which one of these training methods James should use to improve his flexibility for sprint hurdling.

- Static stretching
- Proprioceptive neuromuscular facilitation (PNF).

9 marks

Revision Guide page 11

Hint

When you **evaluate**, you consider various aspects of a subject's qualities in relation to its context, such as: strengths and weaknesses, advantages and disadvantages, pros and cons. You need to come to a judgement supported by evidence, which will often be in the form of a conclusion.

Prepare

You could make a brief plan for longer answers. Here is an example.

- Demonstrate knowledge of the two training methods.
- Evaluate some advantages and disadvantages for how effectively each could improve flexibility for sprint hurdling.
- Conclude by making a judgement about which should be used, evaluating competing points.

Hint

Facilitation means to help. This might be one way of remembering that PNF stretching requires the help of another person to complete.

Watch out!

Relate your answer to the sport in the question so your evaluation is relevant to the question context.

Revision Guide page 11

Hint

For longer answers, use PEEL. For example, in relation to static stretching:

Point: Make one point (for example what static stretching is and how it can be done).

Explain: Explain this point (for example the advantages of the method for James).

Evidence: Justify the point and explanation (for example other considerations relating to this method for James and any disadvantages).

Link: Link back to the question (for example comparing the advantages and benefits of PNF).

Watch out!

Your evaluation should show breadth and not be too brief. Use paragraphs to develop a logical evaluation. Conclude with a judgement as to the most appropriate training method.

Explore

Think about the other components of fitness a sprint hurdler would also need to develop and the training methods they would use. Make sure you are familiar with a range of sports for this component.

....

....

....

....

....

....

....

....

....

....

....

....

....

....

....

....

....

....

....

....

....

....

....

....

....

....

Total for Question 9 = 9 marks

TOTAL FOR PRACTICE ASSESSMENT = 70 MARKS

Practice assessment 4

Answer ALL questions.
Write your answers in the spaces provided.

1. Jon is a mixed martial arts fighter. He takes part in a one-minute sit-up test. His result is **38 reps per minute.**

Table 1 shows the normative test data of the one-minute sit-up test for males and females.

	Category				
Gender	**Excellent**	**Good**	**Average**	**Fair**	**Poor**
Male	>30	26–30	20–25	17–19	<17
Female	>25	21–25	15–20	9–14	<9

Table 1

(a) Identify the category Jon is in for the one-minute sit-up test, using **Table 1**.

....

....

1 mark

(b) State the component of fitness tested by the one-minute sit-up test.

....

....

1 mark

Total for Question 1 = 2 marks

Revision Guide
page 3

Time it!

Time yourself completing this practice assessment. Complete it in **1 hour and 30 minutes**. Check your answers if you have time at the end. Details of the actual assessment may change, so check the latest guidance on the Pearson website to be sure you are up to date.

Hint

When you **identify**, you assess factual information that may require a single-word answer, although sometimes a few words or a maximum of a single sentence are required.

Watch out!

Read the question and Table 1 carefully. When checking Jon's rating, make sure you use the data in the **'male'** row of the table. The information you need is in Table 1 so don't worry if you are unfamiliar with the detail of the sport.

Hint

When you **state**, you give a definition or example – here, the appropriate component of fitness.

Revision Guide pages 12, 13

Time it!

Use the number of marks as a guide to how much time to spend on each question. Question 2 is worth 9 marks overall. See if you can complete parts a–c in around 9–10 minutes, spending around one minute for 1 mark and around two minutes for 2 marks.

Hint

When you **name**, you give a definition or example. Here, you name training methods.

Watch out!

Look at both parts of the question before you start your answer. You need to name **and** describe training methods. Choose the methods you are most confident about describing.

Hint

When you **describe** for this question, you give an account of each training method you have identified.

Hint

When you **give**, you can provide examples, justifications and/or reasons to a context. For Question 2 (b) you give one other benefit of increased self-confidence.

2 Jesse is a very good swimmer and gymnast. He needs excellent strength and speed for his activities.

(a) Complete **Table 2** by:

(i) naming **one** training method to improve each of these components of fitness

(ii) describing how to carry out each of the training methods chosen.

Component of fitness	(i) Training method	(ii) Description of training method
Strength	1 mark	1 mark
Speed	1 mark	1 mark

Table 2

Jesse has high levels of self-confidence. This gives him increased motivation and a positive attitude towards training.

(b) Give **one other** benefit of increased self-confidence.

....

....

1 mark

The coach uses positive reinforcement and organises sessions so that Jesse works with a partner of similar ability.

(c) Explain how these methods can be used to increase Jesse's self-confidence.

Positive reinforcement

....

....

....

....

2 marks

Working with a partner of similar ability

....

....

....

....

2 marks

Total for Question 2 = 9 marks

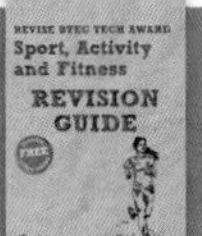

Revision Guide pages 45, 46

Hint

When you **explain**, you convey understanding by making a point/statement or by linking the point/statement with a justification/expansion. Here, you need to make a point by stating what each method is and then expanding on each to show how it will increase self-confidence.

LEARN IT!

Self-confidence can be increased through a positive environment. A positive environment is one where people are not afraid to take chances and make mistakes.

Explore

Think about the reasons self-confidence is important in sport. Consider how being low in self-confidence might negatively affect your performance in your sport.

Explore

Goal setting can increase self-confidence if it is realistic. Consider the principles of goal setting you need to apply to make sure the goals you set are realistic, such as by being SMART (specific, measurable, attainable, relevant, time-framed).

Revision Guide pages 17, 25

Time it!

Question 3 is worth 12 marks overall. See if you can complete all the parts a–f in around 12–15 minutes, spending around two minutes on 2-mark parts and around one minute on 1-mark parts.

Hint

When you **calculate**, you determine the amount or number mathematically. Here, calculate Mackenzie's maximum heart rate (MHR) before calculating the correct percentage of this.

LEARN IT!

To calculate maximum heart rate (MHR) you take the participant's age from 220.

Hint

Training makes the body work harder so it can adapt. It adapts during recovery and repairs any damage caused by training. For Question 3 (b), think what would happen if there wasn't time for adaptation or repair to take place.

LEARN IT!

In addition to the anaerobic training zone, you need to know the training zones for a warm-up (50–60%), fat burning (60–70%) and aerobic exercise (70–80%).

3 Mackenzie is 16. She is training hard to improve her speed so works in her anaerobic training zone. She trains several times a week and is exhausted at the end of each session.

(a) Calculate Mackenzie's anaerobic training zone.

Calculation

....

....

Answer .... bpm

2 marks

(b) Name **two** principles of training that could result if Mackenzie trains too often without enough time for rest.

1 ....

....

2 ....

....

2 marks

Mackenzie works hard in training because she is motivated internally and externally.

(c) State the meaning of the term 'intrinsic motivation'.

....

....

1 mark

Extrinsic motivation can be increased through the use of positive reinforcement.

(d) State the meaning of the term 'positive reinforcement'.

....

....

1 mark

(e) Give **two** examples of the people most likely to give Mackenzie extrinsic motivation.

1 ....

....

2 ....

....

2 marks

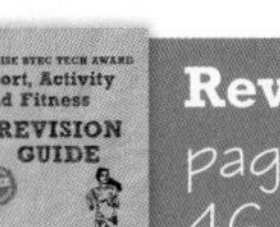

Revision Guide pages 43, 44, 46

LEARN IT!

There are two types of motivation: intrinsic and extrinsic. Extrinsic motivation is when external factors provide the motivation to take part in fitness activity. It can be in the form of tangible or intangible rewards.

Hint

For Question 3 (d), it may help to think about the two words in this term individually. For example, reinforcement is to do with strengthening something. Think about what the coach may want to strengthen and how they do this through positive reinforcement.

Hint

The extrinsic motivation from external factors in Question 3 (e) is from **people**. Think about the people most likely to influence Mackenzie and make her want to train hard.

Revision Guide
pages 47, 48, 49

Watch out!

Read the question carefully. Note that this question is asking for reasons that cause a **drop** in the level of performance.

Hint

Make sure you give two very different reasons in your answer rather than just two examples of the same reason.

Hint

Sports performers can feel cognitive anxiety and somatic anxiety. Somatic anxiety is the physical effects of anxiety, for example, butterflies in the stomach.

Explore

Consider the somatic effects of anxiety and how they might affect performance. Think about the methods to control anxiety and whether some are better suited to controlling cognitive or somatic anxiety.

Mackenzie always performs better in training than in competition.
Her coach says this is because she has high levels of cognitive anxiety.

(f) Explain **two** reasons why cognitive anxiety decreases performance.

1 ....

....

....

....

2 marks

2 ....

....

....

....

2 marks

Total for Question 3 = 12 marks

4 Taylor is using a heart-rate monitor to make sure she is working in the right training zone.

(a) Name the training zone where the percentage of maximum heart rate should be 70–80%.

....

....

1 mark

Taylor applies the FITT principles to her training.

(b) Give the definition of type.

....

....

1 mark

Taylor plans her training sessions carefully as she is aware of the possibility of reversibility.

(c) Describe the training principle of reversibility.

....

....

....

....

2 marks

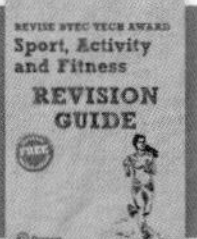

Revision Guide pages 15, 23

Hint

When you train, your body adapts and gets fitter so it can cope with the training. For Question 4 (c), consider what happens if you no longer train.

LEARN IT!

The principles of training are **S**pecificity, **P**rogressive overload, **O**vertraining, **R**eversibility, **T**raining zones (**SPORT**) and participant differences and needs.

Time it!

See if you can answer the **describe** question in around two minutes. There are two marks available so make sure you make two linked points.

Explore

Consider the different methods of training that Taylor could use if she applied the FITT principle 'type' to her training.

Explore

Make sure you know the definitions of the four FITT principles: frequency, intensity, type and time.

Revision Guide pages 20, 24, 29

Two of the principles of training mention the need to match the training to the sport. One of these is participant differences and needs. For Question 4 (e), you need to think of the other one.

Take a single training session out of a six-week training plan. Consider how you would change the session to apply the principles of progressive overload and training thresholds in the next training session.

Consider the main activities you would use in a session if Taylor was training to improve her power.

Explore

Consider the technology used to ensure sportspeople are working at the right training intensity.

Taylor applies the principle of participant differences and needs to her training programme.

(d) Describe the principle of participant differences and needs.

....

....

....

....

2 marks

(e) Identify the principle of training from the following description.

Choosing a training method that develops a specific component of fitness which benefits participation in sport or activity.

....

....

1 mark

Total for Question 4 = 7 marks

5 Zara competes in the high jump and is training to improve her power and body composition.

(a) State the normal recommended percentage of fat in the diet.

.... %

1 mark

(b) Zara's diet is 50% fat.

(i) Describe how Zara's diet will affect her body composition.

....

....

....

....

2 marks

(ii) Explain **one** possible effect of Zara's diet on her high jump performance.

....

....

....

....

2 marks

Revision Guide
pages 8, 31, 36

Hint

Read each question carefully and notice information that helps to inform your answer. For Question 5, you are told the event is high jump. Think about what you do in high jump and why what you eat is important.

LEARN IT!

Fats are one of three different types of macronutrients you need to eat in your diet. They are called macronutrients as you need to eat large quantities of them to remain healthy.

Time it!

See if you can answer Question 5 (b) (ii) in around two minutes. **First** make **one** point and **then** explain it.

Explore

Think about the body composition of elite performers in different sports. Consider whether a particular body composition appears beneficial in some sports and why this might be. Think about how each macronutrient (carbohydrates, protein, fats) helps a sports performer.

Revision Guide pages 36, 41

Hint

Although an individual jump is over very quickly, high jump competitions can take a long time to complete. The high jumpers will spend quite a bit of time waiting for their next jump.

LEARN IT!

There are two types of fat, saturated and unsaturated. Saturated fats are found in red meat, milk and cheese and can be harmful to health as they can increase the total cholesterol in the body.

Explore

Think about the changes long-distance runners could make to their diet **before**, **during** and **after** their activity to help improve their performance.

Explore

Consider why an increase in cholesterol from saturated fats can lead to ill health, and some specific health risks associated with high cholesterol, such as coronary heart disease.

(c) Explain why the type of fat in Zara's diet and the timing of her food intake can aid her performance during and after a long athletics competition.

Type of fat in the diet

....

....

....

....

2 marks

Timing of food intake

....

....

....

....

2 marks

Total for Question 5 = 9 marks

6 Aafiya takes part in exercise regularly as part of her healthy lifestyle. She also makes sure she eats a balanced, healthy diet.

(a) State the percentage of dietary intake that should be carbohydrate in a healthy diet.

.....................................%

1 mark

Minerals, for example potassium, are also an essential part of Aafiya's diet.

(b) Identify **one other** mineral Aafiya should eat in her diet.

....

....

1 mark

(c) Explain how having the right amount of potassium in her diet will help Aafiya in her performance.

....

....

....

....

2 marks

Potassium is found in potatoes and yoghurt.

(d) Name **two other** food sources of potassium.

1 ....

....

2 ....

....

2 marks

Total for Question 6 = 6 marks

Revision Guide pages 31, 38

LEARN IT!

The three types of **macronutrients** are carbohydrate, fat and protein. They are called macronutrients as we have to eat large quantities of them in our diet.

LEARN IT!

Vitamins and minerals are **micronutrients**. They should be eaten in very small quantities but are essential to health.

Time it!

See if you can answer Question 6 (d) in less than two minutes. Make sure you give two **different** responses.

Explore

Consider the function and sources of vitamins A, B1, C and D. Think about how each of these vitamins can aid a sports performer.

Explore

Fibre is an important part of the diet although it does not provide nutrients. Consider the different sources of fibre you should eat, and why.

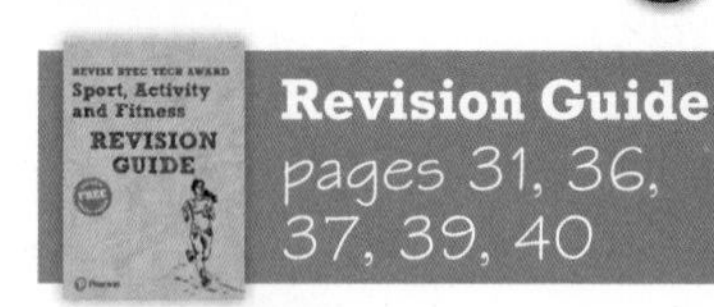

Revision Guide pages 31, 36, 37, 39, 40

Hint

When you **analyse**, you examine something methodically and in detail, typically in order to explain, interpret or communicate something. Here, you examine the table to see which foods contain fats, vitamin B1 and fluid intake. You then consider how the function of each would help a hockey player.

Time it!

This **analyse** question requires a longer answer that may take around 9–10 minutes.

Prepare

You could make a brief plan for longer answers, roughly dividing your time. Here is an example.

- Fats: amount of fat vs RDA; type of fat with examples of sources; benefit to Wei's hockey performance (three minutes)
- Vitamin B1: sources and role of vitamin B1; benefit to Wei's hockey performance (three minutes)
- Fluid intake: quantity of fluid; recommendations; benefit to Wei's hockey performance (three minutes).

7 Wei is a hockey player.

Table 3 shows Wei's dietary intake and the percentage of fats eaten on a typical day.

Daily percentage of fats in diet: 25–30%	
Breakfast	Bran flakes with skimmed milk 25 cl of orange juice
Mid-morning snack	Pumpkin seeds and almonds 25 cl of water
Lunch	Avocado salad 50 cl of water
Afternoon snack	1 apple and 1 orange 25 cl of a glucose drink
Dinner	Pork with rice 50 cl of water and 25 cl of a fizzy drink

Table 3

Analyse, using **Table 3,** how Wei's dietary intake of fats, vitamin B1 and fluid intake will benefit his performance as a hockey player.

9 marks

....

....

....

....

....

....

....

....

....

....

....

....

....

....

....

....

Revision Guide pages 31, 36, 37, 39, 40

Total for Question 7 = 9 marks

Watch out!

You don't need to analyse all the foods in Table 3, only the nutrients and fluid mentioned in the question.

Hint

For longer answers, use PEEL. For example, relating to fat:

Point: Make one point (for example the RDA of fat).

Explain: Explain this point (explain what this means in terms of Wei's intake, weight and sport).

Evidence: Justify the point and explanation (for example the impact on Wei's performance if under/over the RDA).

Link: Link back to the question (for example benefits of intake for Wei's hockey performance).

LEARN IT!

You have to eat foods that contain vitamin B1 every day as it cannot be stored in the body.

Hint

To check whether the daily recommended fluid intake is met, remember there are 100 cl in a litre so 25 cl is a quarter of a litre.

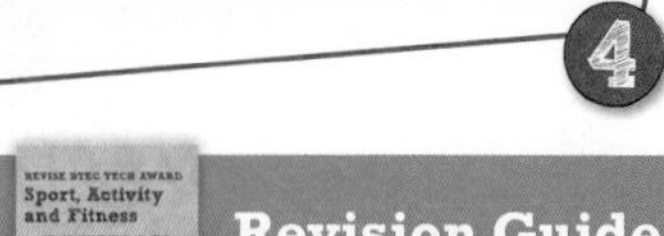

Revision Guide pages 47, 48

Hint

If asked to state **differences** between two things, don't just say what one is. For each of these **two** differences, you could use words such as **rather than** or **but in** to make it clear how they differ.

Hint

Read the question introduction carefully. For example, you are told that Cody's personality means he finds all situations stressful. This informs the right choice for Question 8 (b).

Watch out!

Read each question carefully. In Question 8 (c), the **focus** has changed to **somatic** anxiety.

LEARN IT!

For Question 8 (d), cognitive effects of anxiety are the ways you are affected **psychologically** rather than physically.

Watch out!

Question 8 (d) includes the effect of **feeling worried.** Your answer should state **two other** cognitive effects of anxiety.

8 Cody has the skills to be a good badminton player, but his personality means that he finds all situations stressful. This means when he plays badminton, he worries about how well he is playing and feels sick, so his performance suffers.

(a) State **two** differences between state and trait anxiety.

1 ....

....

2 ....

....

2 marks

(b) Explain which type of anxiety Cody is experiencing.

....

....

....

....

2 marks

Due to Cody's level of anxiety, his badminton performance is poor.

(c) State **one** possible effect of somatic anxiety on Cody during a game of badminton.

....

....

1 mark

Feeling worried is a cognitive effect of anxiety.

(d) State **two other** cognitive effects of anxiety.

1 ....

....

2 ....

....

2 marks

Total for Question 8 = 7 marks

9 Camille plays badminton.

Figure 1 shows Camille's partially completed fitness programme.

Personal information			
Name and age: Camille, 16	**Health screening questionnaire results:** Healthy	**Activity dislikes:** Interval training	**Activity likes:** Working with others Game-based activities
Aim: To be quicker in my movement around the court so I miss fewer shuttles			
Objective: To take part in three badminton training sessions a week			
Components of fitness: Speed		**Safe design:**	
Session plans			
Warm-up: Pulse raiser, mobiliser, stretch	**Main activity:** SAQ® session	**Cool-down:** Pulse lowering and stretch	

Figure 1

A fitness programme requires a set structure to ensure it is effective in achieving the aim of the participant.

Analyse the importance of including health-screening questionnaires and of selecting appropriate components of fitness for training and training methods, in order to achieve Camille's aim.

9 marks

....

....

....

....

....

....

....

....

....

....

....

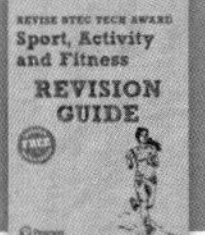

Revision Guide pages 12, 26, 27

Hint

When you **analyse**, you examine something methodically and in detail to explain, interpret or communicate something. Here, you need to examine the components of the fitness programme to see how important they are in achieving Camille's aim to be quicker in movement around the badminton court.

Time it!

This **analyse** question requires a longer answer that may take around 9–10 minutes.

Prepare

You could make a brief plan for longer answers, roughly dividing your time. Here is an example.

Analyse the importance of:

- health-screening questionnaires (three minutes)
- selecting appropriate components of fitness for training and training methods to achieve Camille's aim (three minutes)
- the purpose and suitability of the selection in relation to Camille's aims and sport (three minutes).

Revision Guide
pages 12, 27

Hint

For longer answers, use PEEL. For example, relating to speed:

Point: Make one point (for example the component of fitness to meet Camille's aim).

Explain: Explain this point (for example how this component helps meet the aim).

Evidence: Justify the point and explanation (for example why this component is relevant, rather than others).

Link: Link back to the question (for example the importance and benefits for Camille to achieve her aim).

Hint

Consider different training methods Camille could choose to improve speed and those appropriate for her sport of badminton.

LEARN IT!

SAQ® – standing for **speed, agility and quickness** – is a training method for improving speed.

Time it!

You should have completed Practice assessment 4 in no more than **1 hour and 30 minutes.** Ensure you have answered all the questions and given all the information asked for. Check your answers if you have time.

....

....

....

....

....

....

....

....

....

....

....

....

....

....

....

....

....

....

....

....

....

....

....

....

....

Total for Question 9 = 9 marks

TOTAL FOR PRACTICE ASSESSMENT = 70 MARKS

Answers

Use this section to check your answers.

- For questions with clear correct answers, these are provided.
- For questions where individual responses may be phrased in different ways or where there may be more than one correct answer, this is noted along with example answers.
- For questions that require longer answers, bullet points are provided to indicate key points you could include in your answer, or how your answer could be structured. **Your answer should be written using sentences and paragraphs** and might include some of these points but not necessarily all of them.

> The questions and sample answers are provided to help you revise content and skills. Ask your tutor or check the Pearson website for the most up-to-date Sample Assessment Material, past papers and mark schemes to get an indication of the actual assessment and what this requires of you. Details of the actual assessment may change so always make sure you are up to date.

Practice assessment 1

(pages 1–16)

1. (a) Below average

(b) Flexibility

2. (a) Individual responses. For example:

Method of training 1: Plyometrics. **Reason:** Involves jumping which is needed to clear the hurdles.

Method of training 2: Anaerobic hill sprint training. **Reason:** Involves running as fast as possible which is needed when sprinting between hurdles.

(b) Individual responses. For example:

1 He may receive praise from his coach.

2 He may get a prize for regular attendance from the coach.

(c) Individual responses. For example:

1 He will continue to take part on a regular basis.

2 He will be less likely to give up even if finding the training difficult.

3. (a) Frequency

(b) Aerobic endurance

(c) Cool-down

(d) Intrinsic motivation

(e) Individual responses. For example:

1 Ivan will display a more positive attitude to his training, increasing his belief that he will achieve his training goal.

2 Ivan's concentration and effort will improve when training, improving his performance so he will feel better about his ability.

(f) Individual responses. For example:

1 The coach could praise Ivan when he does something well in training or tries hard.

2 The coach can be careful not to criticise Ivan when he does something wrong so Ivan will feel more relaxed in training and therefore more likely to try harder because he will not be afraid of being criticised for making mistakes.

4. (a) Individual responses. For example:

Intensity: How hard she is working during the session.

Example: She is currently using a 4 kg medicine ball to complete the drills. She could increase this to a 5 kg ball.

Type: An appropriate type of training method selected to improve the component of fitness she needs to improve for her sport.

Example: She is using plyometrics to increase her leg power for volleyball.

(b) Individual responses. For example:

Participant differences and needs: Choosing a component of fitness based on fitness test data and relating the chosen fitness method to the person's sport or activity.

Example: She has identified a weakness in her power, so to improve it she chooses plyometric training, which like volleyball involves a lot of jumping.

Training zones: Working at the correct training zone of intensity of maximum heart rate to experience fitness improvement.

Example: When she trains, she needs to make sure her heart rate is in the anaerobic training zone of 80–100%.

5. (a) 2000 calories (kcal)

(b)–(f) Individual responses. For example:

(b) Eggs

(c) To repair microtears in her muscles caused by a strenuous tennis match

(d) An avocado

(e) If she eats too much fat it can cause an increase in cholesterol in the walls of the arteries leading to an increased risk of heart attack.

(f) To maintain her eyesight to assist her hand–eye coordination necessary to hit the tennis ball.

6. (a) Dehydration

(b) 1 His blood plasma volume will reduce.

2 His ability to sweat will be reduced.

(c) Individual responses. For example: His blood plasma remains thinner so his body can continue to transport oxygen to his muscles during the race.

(d) Individual responses. For example: He might drink isotonic drinks as these contain some carbohydrates, giving him additional energy during the race.

7. Individual responses. Your answer should show accurate and detailed knowledge and understanding. Your points should be relevant to the context in the question, with clear links. Your discussion should be well developed and logical, clearly considering different aspects and how they interrelate.

Your discussion should include the following aspects, for example:

- **Caffeine** will increase energy levels.
- Energy is important in physical activity as it will allow Ethan to train.
- The more energy Ethan has, the harder he should be able to work in his training. Therefore if he takes caffeine before his training session he should be able to work harder in training, improving his performance.
- **Glucose tablets** contain high levels of carbohydrates and are quick to eat.
- Glucose will increase Ethan's energy quickly. However if he takes them too soon before he starts training it may have the opposite effect to the desired one. This is because the increase in glucose will cause blood glucose levels to drop leaving him feeling tired. He therefore may want to take this supplement during the session rather than too long before it.
- **Creatine** is a protein supplement.

- Protein is needed to increase muscle mass and to recover after exercise. This would be good for Ethan because he needs to build as much muscle mass as possible to increase the amount of weights that he can lift.
- Ethan should also consider using his own diet to achieve the same effects in training. For example a properly balanced diet will provide the energy he needs without the need for additional caffeine or glucose tablets. He could even have a cup of coffee or tea before training.
- Also, sometimes supplements have sugar added to make them taste nicer. If they do, this could lead to weight gain if Ethan has a lot of them.

8. (a) Individual responses. For example: When the performer is tense and apprehensive all the time. It is a characteristic of their personality and therefore anxiety is a consistent feeling for them.

(b) Individual responses. For example: If they draw, this will create a worrying situation for Aiden meaning that he will find this situation stressful. His state anxiety will increase in case he is selected to take one of the penalties.

(c) Individual responses. For example:

1 Let them play music in the changing rooms or on the way to the match, so the players focus on the music rather than worrying about the game and the possibility of penalties.

2 Give the team a pre-match talk to help reduce their anxiety, focusing on the team's strengths and how well they have done with penalties in the past, to reassure them they can do well.

9. Individual responses. Your answer should show accurate, detailed knowledge and understanding. Your points should be relevant to the context in the question, with clear links. Your evaluation should be well developed and logical, clearly considering different aspects and competing points in detail, leading to a conclusion that is fully supported.

Your evaluation should include the following aspects, for example:

The basic features of each training method, for example:

- Interval training is repeated sets of higher intensity exercise with lower intensity periods for recovery to allow the performer to work at higher intensity again. To work aerobically Jenna should be working at 60–80% HRM. As Jenna's aerobic endurance improves, she will be able to work for longer intervals with shorter rest or recovery periods.
- Fartlek training is where you exercise at different intensities and use different terrains to increase intensity of the session.

Some advantages of each training method, for example:

- The advantage of interval training is that it can be carried out in the swimming pool. Jenna could swim a number of lengths, rest and then repeat.
- Fartlek training is designed to improve aerobic endurance. This would therefore be a good training method for Jenna as this is the component of fitness she needs to improve. It will also help her develop some speed during the higher intensity parts of the session.

Some disadvantages of each training method, for example:

- The main disadvantage of interval training is that Jenna needs access to the pool to carry out this training so can't just train whenever she wants.
- An issue with fartlek training is that it is not as sport specific. She would use this method of training when running at different intensities over different terrains. The terrain in the pool is unchanging and does not involve running.

A supported conclusion considering both competing points, for example:

- While both training methods have advantages and disadvantages, as Jenna trains regularly with her swimming club giving her easy access to a pool, she should use interval training because she can make it more sport specific.

Practice assessment 2

(pages 17–32)

1. (a) Excellent

(b) Strength

2. (a) Individual responses. For example:

Training method: Continuous training **Description:** Running at 60–80% of HRM for at least 30 minutes.

Training method: Plyometrics **Description:** Box jumping where the leg muscles lengthen as you jump down from the box and then quickly contract maximally to jump onto the next box.

(b) Individual responses. For example: How worried or nervous a participant is.

(c) Individual responses. For example:

Induction: The coach will familiarise Owen with the facilities and the equipment at the club, removing Owen's fear of the unknown so he will be less anxious.

Ability level: Owen knows that he will be put in the same group as other beginners so this reduces his anxiety because he will feel that he should be able to do as well as the others.

3. (a) **Calculation:** RPE x 10 = HR (bpm), therefore 15 x 10 = 150 bpm. **Answer: 150 bpm**

(b) Individual responses. For example:

1 In his wrist

2 In his neck

(c) Extrinsic reward

(d) Individual responses. For example: non-physical rewards

(e) Individual responses. For example:

1 Praise from the coach for a personal best.

2 Recognition from other athletes as being a good athlete.

(f) Individual responses. For example:

Continuing to take part: Ali will not miss training, so his body will continue to adapt, increasing his fitness.

Increased rewards: The rewards will give Ali even more reason to train, so he will get even more out of the training, putting in greater effort to increase his fitness further.

4. (a) Warm-up zone

(b) Individual responses. For example: How often you train.

(c) Individual responses. For example: Being aware of the risk of injury due to fatigue from increasing training workload too quickly.

(d) Individual responses. For example: Choosing a training method that develops a specific component of fitness to meet the needs and demands of a specific sport.

(e) Participant differences and needs

5. (a) 1 litre

(b) Individual responses. For example:

(i) There will be less water available for the blood plasma, making the plasma thicker.

(ii) The blood plasma will not work as effectively in transporting oxygen so Paul will have less energy for his training, reducing the amount he can do.

(c) Individual responses. For example:

1 Paul will be able to maintain his core body temperature at 37° C so that he doesn't overheat and therefore need to slow down when running.

2 His joints will remain lubricated so that his running action remains effective to help him maintain his time.

6. (a) 12–15%

(b) Individual responses. For example: Chicken

(c) Individual responses. For example: Maddie's strength training will produce micro-tears in her muscles and the protein will repair these and increase the strength of the muscle so Maddie can use her increased explosive strength to jump higher in the game.

(d) 1 Essential

2 Non-essential

7. Individual responses. Your answer should show accurate knowledge and understanding. Your analysis should break the situation down into component parts and your points should be relevant to the context in the question. Your analysis should be well developed and logical, clearly considering the different aspects and how they interrelate. Your analysis should include the following aspects, for example:

For each stated vitamin, the source (based on the table), the function and the application to the question context.

- Layla gets vitamin A in her diet when she eats liver at dinner.
- The apple and orange in her diet will provide her with vitamin C.
- Tuna is an oily fish so she will get vitamin D from this.
- These nutrients are essential due to their function. For example, vitamin A maintains normal eyesight and is therefore important to her hand–eye coordination.
- Without good hand–eye coordination she would not be able to adjust her feet position to get in the right place while at the same time swinging her badminton racket to make a good connection with the shuttle.
- Vitamin C is important as it will maintain her immune system.
- A good immune system means that she will be less likely to get things like colds which could prevent her from training, causing her fitness and therefore performance to get worse.
- Vitamin D is needed to keep bones and muscles healthy.
- Without enough vitamin D she could become injured. If she is injured she will be unable to train and be likely to suffer reversibility.

8. (a) Individual responses. For example:

1 Trait anxiety is related to someone's personality, whereas state anxiety is related to the situation.

2 Trait anxiety is a constant feeling of anxiety, whereas state anxiety is constantly changing as the situation changes.

(b) Individual responses. For example: Finn is experiencing state anxiety because he is concerned about taking the free throw.

(c) Individual responses. For example: Cognitive anxiety is the psychological effects of anxiety.

(d) 1 Muscle tension

2 Increased sweat rate

9. Individual responses. Your answer should show accurate knowledge and understanding. Your analysis should break the situation down into component parts and your points should be relevant to the context in the question. Your analysis should be well developed and logical, clearly considering the different aspects and how they interrelate.

Your analysis should include the following aspects, for example:

Demonstrate knowledge of a person-centred approach with personal information

- A person-centred approach to exercise will capture Monica's exercise availability. This is important so that the programme can be designed around activities she can do when she has the free time to exercise.
- A person-centred approach would also note the types of activities Monica likes to do. In this case Monica doesn't like to do continuous road running but she is happy with any other training method.
- By knowing when she can train and what types of training methods she likes to do, a programme can be put together that is possible to follow because it is set at the right times, and is also likely to be followed because Monica enjoys the sorts of training activities that are listed.

Importance of aims

- It is essential to have an aim, as the training programme should be specifically designed with this aim in mind.
- If there is no clear aim then training is less likely to be focused and although Monica may carry out a lot of fitness sessions, she may not improve the area of fitness she needs to improve. She may also lack motivation because she isn't sure of the purpose of her training.
- Based on the objective in the partially completed fitness programme, Monica's likely aim would be to increase her fitness so that she can maintain the quality of her play throughout the game.

Importance of a warm-up

- A warm-up will help prepare the body for exercise.
- The warm-up should include a pulse raiser, a mobiliser and stretching of the muscles to be used in the game.
- If her muscles and ligaments have already been stretched the amount they will be stretched in the game, Monica will be ready to play and less likely to become injured.

Practice assessment 3

(pages 33–48)

1. (a) Excellent

(b) Power

2. (a) Individual responses. For example:

Method of training 1: Circuit training. **Reason:** Can target his arm muscles, setting up stations to focus on the same muscles he uses when rowing.

Method of training 2: Core stability training. **Reason:** Can use this training method to work his stomach and back muscles as he will need to use these to maintain the correct seated position in the boat to row effectively.

(b) Individual responses. For example:

1 Butterflies in his stomach

2 Increased heart rate

(c) Individual responses. For example:

1 The coach could let Karar listen to music before the competition.

2 The coach could make sure that the opposition are in the same league so Karar feels he is competing at the right level.

3. (a) Rate of perceived exertion (RPE)

(b) Individual responses. For example: Progressive overload through increased frequency

(c) Individual responses. For example: To increase her heart rate

(d) Extrinsic motivation

(e) Individual responses. For example:

1 As Jenny is highly motivated, she will push herself harder in training so she exercises at a higher intensity.

2 Training can sometimes be boring, but Jenny will ignore this and not drop out, continuing to take part on a regular basis so her fitness continues to increase.

(f) Individual responses. For example:

1 The instructor could give Jenny a certificate of attendance if she attends every session.

2 The instructor could have a competition for the most improved person and offer a prize to the winner. This would encourage Jenny to train harder to win the prize.

4. (a) Individual responses. For example:

Time: How long the person trains for. It should be long enough to encourage progressive overload.

Example: He might increase the time spent training from 45 minutes to 50 minutes.

Frequency: How many training sessions he goes to in a week.

Example: At the moment he goes once a week, but he might increase this and go twice a week.

(b) Individual responses. For example:

Reversibility: When any improvements in fitness are lost as the person can no longer train as hard or often.

Example: He may have twisted an ankle during training and have to miss training sessions, meaning his speed will decrease.

Overtraining: When the training workload is increased too quickly, not giving the body time to recover between training sessions.

Example: He increases his training load from one day a week to five days a week.

5. (a) Protein is made up of amino acids.

(b) Individual responses. For example: Soya beans

(c) Individual responses. For example: During the hard training session the tendons and ligaments will get damaged. These need protein to fully repair so Mo can train again the next day without increased risk of injury.

(d) Individual responses. For example: Brown rice

(e) Individual responses. For example: It will allow Mo to remove the waste from his body before he exercises so that he is more comfortable during the long event.

(f) Individual responses. For example: To reduce the chance of him becoming ill by fighting bacterial infections.

6. (a) Individual responses. For example: Dairy products

(b) Individual responses. For example:

1 Reduction in bone strength

2 Increased risk of injury to the skeletal system in tackles

(c) Individual responses. For example: Iron increases the body's ability to carry oxygen so she will get more oxygen to her muscles allowing her to work aerobically for longer.

(d) Individual responses. For example: Bananas are a good source of potassium which helps regulate body fluid levels so she is at less risk of becoming dehydrated.

7. Individual responses. Your answer should show accurate and detailed knowledge and understanding. Your points should be relevant to the context in the question, with clear links. Your discussion should be well developed and logical, clearly considering different aspects and how they interrelate.

Your discussion should include the following aspects, for example:

- She is eating just under the **recommended daily calorie allowance** for a normal person on some of the days.
- This could mean she isn't eating enough calories, as during exercise she will burn more calories than a normal person.
- Eating too few calories would result in weight loss or lack of energy to train. However if she is currently overweight, this could help as she would reduce excess weight, making training less demanding.
- She has a **good balance of macronutrients**, 55–58% carbohydrates, 30% fats and 12–15% protein.
- It is important she does not exceed this percentage of fats as this could have health issues for her, for example increased risk of CHD.
- Also, with more fats she may have fewer carbohydrates, which are a very good source of energy. She will need a lot of these to have energy for her training sessions.
- A smaller percentage of protein would not be good as she needs protein for growth and repair of her muscles so her fitness can continue to improve.
- She drinks 2 litres of water on the days she is not training and 4 litres on the days that she does train.
- **Correct fluid intake** means she should be hydrated so that she can train effectively.
- If she drinks less than this, she may become dehydrated leading to her overheating when training.

8. (a) The belief that a desired behaviour can be performed.

(b) Individual responses. For example: The self-confidence will give her a positive attitude towards the game. She will be more assertive in the goal area, believing she can save any shot so not afraid to try to make difficult saves.

(c) Individual responses. For example:

1 In training she could set a realistic goal to increase the number of aerial saves she makes. When she acheives this goal she will be more confident about attempting these types of saves.

2 If she sets measurable goals and then achieves them she will know she is performing better, and this will increase her self-confidence.

9. Individual responses. Your answer should show accurate, detailed knowledge and understanding. Your points should be relevant to the context in the question, with clear links. Your evaluation should be well developed and logical, clearly considering different aspects and competing points in detail, leading to a conclusion that is fully supported.

Your evaluation should include the following aspects, for example:

The basic features of each training method, for example:

- Static stretching can be done independently or with another person. The athlete can target a specific muscle or muscle group by stretching a muscle and holding the stretch for over 12 seconds.
- PNF stretching needs the help of another person to hold the stretch whilst the athlete pushes against the person holding the stretch.
- The athlete then relaxes the muscle and the person helping stretches the muscle a little further. This is repeated three times.

Some advantages of each training method, for example:

- One advantage of static stretching is that you can tailor it to any sport, so James could target his hips in particular to make them flexible enough to achieve the low position over the hurdles. Also, you don't need any specialist equipment and can do it on your own so James wouldn't need to be reliant on anyone else being available when he wanted to train.
- PNF helps to develop flexibility at a faster rate than any other training method, so James would see better results sooner. It too needs minimal equipment.

Some disadvantages of each training method, for example:

- The main disadvantage with static stretching is that it will be limited in terms of increasing his flexibility. This is because it only uses the regular range of motion for the muscle at the joint.
- An issue with PNF stretching is that the person helping needs to be experienced so that they know how far to stretch the muscle, otherwise they would cause James an injury, meaning that he could not race.

A supported conclusion considering both competing points, for example:

- While both training methods have advantages and disadvantages, as James needs to increase his flexibility in order to get better, he should use PNF, provided he has an experienced person to help him. This way his flexibility will increase faster and his sprint hurdling time will improve.

Practice assessment 4

(pages 49–64)

1. (a) Excellent

(b) Muscular endurance

2 (a) Individual responses. For example:

Name of training method: Free weights

Description of training method: Weights that are not attached to machinery, for example dumbbells.

Name of training method: Sprint training

Description of training method: Running a short distance as fast as possible on a flat surface.

(b) Individual responses. For example: Jesse will have improved concentration when training.

(c) Individual responses. For example:

Positive reinforcement. This is a form of extrinsic motivation. This will help self-confidence because Jesse will feel good that the coach is recognising his hard work.

Working with a partner of similar ability. Because your training partner is a similar ability you can keep up with each other, getting better together. This helps self-confidence as you won't feel you are of a poor ability because you are evenly matched, rather than partnering up with someone who is a lot better.

3. (a) **Calculation:**

MHR = 220 – age (16) = 204

80% of MHR = 204 x 80/100 = 163

So 100% of MHR = 204 bpm; 80% of MHR = 163 bpm

Answer: 163 bpm

(b) 1 Overtraining

2 Reversibility

(c) Individual responses. For example: Motivation that comes from internal factors.

(d) Individual responses. For example: The coach giving encouragement when the performer does something well.

(e) Individual responses. For example:

1 Her coach

2 The other people she trains with

(f) Individual responses. For example:

1 Mackenzie's cognitive anxiety is brought on by her state anxiety. She will feel worried about the competition so not perform as well as she can.

2 Due to the cognitive anxiety she will have trouble sleeping because of thinking about the competition. The lack of sleep will leave her tired so her performance will suffer.

4. (a) Aerobic

(b) Individual responses. For example: Type is the training method that is chosen and the exercises used in the training method.

(c) Individual responses. For example: Reversibility is when you can't train due to injury or illness and this leads to a reduction in fitness.

(d) Individual responses. For example: Principle of participant differences and needs means Taylor will select training methods to work on relevant components of fitness for her sport, based on her fitness test results.

(e) Specificity

5. (a) 30%

(b) (i) Individual responses. For example: Body composition is the percentage of stored fat in the body compared to muscle mass. If Zara eats more fat, she could increase the percentage of her body that is fat.

(b) (ii) Individual responses. For example: If Zara eats too much fat, she could gain weight. This will mean she has to work harder to lift her body weight over the bar so she may not be able to jump as high.

(c) Individual responses. For example:

Type of fat in the diet: If Zara eats fats in her diet, she can use them as an energy source while she is resting between jumps so that she doesn't fatigue. She should eat unsaturated fats rather than saturated fats as these will be better for her health.

Timing of food intake: By eating protein about an hour after the competition she will repair any damage to her muscles caused by the session, so she is ready to train again.

6. (a) 50–60%

(b) Individual responses. For example: Iron

(c) Individual responses. For example: Potassium regulates fluid levels so will help Aafiya remain hydrated so she can maintain her body temperature during exercise.

(d) 1 Bananas

2 Sunflower seeds

7. Individual responses. Your answer should show accurate knowledge and understanding. Your analysis should break the situation down into component parts and your points should be relevant to the context in the question. Your analysis should be well developed and logical, clearly considering the different aspects and how they interrelate.

Your analysis should include the following points, for example.

Fats and benefit to performance as a hockey player:

- The amount of fat Wei is eating is within the recommended daily allowance so he should not have any health issues as a result of this, meaning he should not need to miss training due to ill health.
- Wei is making good choices about the types of fat he is eating as the majority are sources of unsaturated fats, for example the nuts and avocados he eats.
- This is better for his performance as they provide a good aerobic energy source for the body and as he isn't eating too many, he should not gain weight. Gaining excess weight would make training more challenging as he would have more body weight to carry when moving.

Vitamin B1 and benefits to performance as a hockey player:

- The bran Wei eats at breakfast will provide him with vitamin B1, and as he has it with skimmed milk, he will minimise the saturated fats he consumes, reducing the risk of high cholesterol.

- Vitamin B1 is very important to Wei as it converts food into energy.
- Wei needs energy to carry out training and to compete at his best level of performance as a hockey player.
- If Wei doesn't have enough energy, he will show signs of fatigue and his hockey performance will get worse.

Fluid intake and benefits to performance as a hockey player:

- Wei is drinking enough fluid, at 2 litres each day. However this doesn't show any additional fluid intake on the days he trains.
- It is important to remain hydrated, otherwise during the game Wei may overheat as he will not sweat effectively.
- Good hydration will also mean that Wei's blood plasma will be thinner, improving oxygen transport to his muscles.
- This will allow him to work at a higher level for longer during a hockey match or during training.

8 (a) Individual responses. For example:

1 State anxiety is situation specific rather than trait anxiety which is more a personality characteristic.

2 With trait anxiety the performer is anxious all the time but in state anxiety they are only anxious in specific high-pressure situations.

(b) Individual responses. For example: He is experiencing trait anxiety because he finds all situations stressful, not just badminton.

(c) Individual responses. For example: He may increase the amount he sweats.

(d) Individual responses. For example:

1 Poor concentration levels

2 Lack of sleep due to overthinking

9 Individual responses. Your answer should show accurate knowledge and understanding. Your analysis should break the situation down into component parts and your points should be relevant to the context in the question. Your analysis should be well developed and logical, clearly considering the different aspects and how they interrelate.

Your analysis should include the following aspects, for example:

Importance of including health-screening questionnaires:

- Health-screening questionnaires are part of a person-centred approach.
- Health-screening questionnaires give personal information about the participant's health.
- This is really important because someone's medical history might indicate that they shouldn't participate in physical activity if they have a known heart condition or a history of it in the family.

Selecting appropriate components of fitness for training and training methods to achieve her aim:

- As Camille doesn't have any health issues, she just needs to consider her main aim and how selecting appropriate components of fitness and training methods will help her achieve her aim.
- Camille has a main aim that she wants to achieve. To do this she must think about the components of fitness she needs to improve. These could be components she is already scoring 'good' at not just ones where she has a rating of low.
- She should carry out fitness tests to measure her fitness, but she should also think about the sport and what she wants to do.
- There would be no point in Camille working on her aerobic endurance, even though this is important in badminton, as she wants to be able to move faster, which means she needs to work on her speed and agility.
- Camille's opponents will be trying to hit the shuttle somewhere on the court where Camille isn't. Therefore not only does she need to be fast, but she also needs to be able to turn and change direction quickly. It would seem therefore that Camille has made a good choice of the component she wants to improve based on her aim.
- Training methods are used to improve the components of fitness.
- Training methods are designed to work a particular aspect of fitness, so by doing the training method she should improve that area of fitness.
- If she chooses the wrong training method, she would develop a different component of fitness. Alternatively, she might develop the right component of fitness, but the training might not be as relevant to her sport as another method. For example, cross-country runners would choose fartlek rather than continuous training. Both methods would improve aerobic endurance, but fartlek is more appropriate to their activity.
- Camille should choose SAQ® as her training method as this is sport-specific speed training, so she could base it on the movements she has to make around the badminton court.

Notes

Notes

Notes

Notes

Notes

Notes